Health Policy

The Politics of Decision Making

Weber State University School of Nursing Custom Text

Nursing 4300: Healthcare Policy and Decision Making

JONES & BARTLETT
LEARNING

World Headquarters
Jones & Bartlett Learning
5 Wall Street
Burlington, MA 01803
978-443-5000
info@jblearning.com
www.jblearning.com

Jones & Bartlett Learning books and products are available through most bookstores and online booksellers. To contact Jones & Bartlett Learning directly, call 800-832-0034, fax 978-443-8000, or visit our website, www.jblearning.com.

This book is produced through PUBLISH – a custom publishing service offered by Jones & Bartlett Learning. For more information on PUBLISH, contact us at 800-832-0034 or visit our website at www.jblearning.com.

Disclaimer
This publication is sold with the understanding that the publisher is not engaged in rendering medical, legal, accounting, or other professional services. If medical, legal, accounting, or other professional service advice is required, the service of a competent professional should be sought. The authors, editor, and publisher have designed this publication to provide accurate information with regard to the subject matter covered. However, they are not responsible for errors, omissions, or for any outcomes related to the use of the contents of this publication and make no guarantee and assume no responsibility or liability for the use of the products and procedures described, or the correctness, sufficiency, or completeness of stated information, opinions, or recommendations. Treatments and side effects described in this publication are not applicable to all people; required dosages and experienced side effects will vary among individuals. Drugs and medical devices discussed herein are controlled by the Food and Drug Administration (FDA) and may have limited availability for use only in research studies or clinical trials. Research, clinical practice, and government regulations often change accepted standards. When consideration is being given to the use of any drug in the clinical setting, the health care provider or reader is responsible for determining FDA status of the drug, reading the package insert, and reviewing prescribing information for the most current recommendations on dose, precautions, and contraindications and for determining the appropriate usage for the product. This is especially important in the case of drugs that are new or seldom used. Any references in this publication to procedures to be employed when rendering emergency care to the sick and injured are provided solely as a general guide; other or additional safety measures might be required under particular circumstances. This publication is not intended as a statement of the standards of care required in any particular situation; circumstances and the physical conditions of patients can vary widely from one emergency to another. This publication is not intended in any way to advise emergency personnel concerning their legal authority to perform the activities or procedures discussed. Such local determination should be made only with the aid of legal counsel. Some images in this publication feature models; these models do not necessarily endorse, represent, or participate in the activities represented in the images.

Cover Image: © Photos.com

6048
Printed in the United States of America
16 15 14 13   10 9 8 7 6 5 4 3 2

Contents

Policy Overview

Policy and political processes are strategies that nurses and other healthcare professionals can use to implement community- and societal-level change. Policy development and formulation are considered population-based interventions useful in impacting the nation's health. Policy is not random but purpose and goal driven. Policy and politics are interrelated concepts. Policy determines politics and politics determines policy.

Nurses and other healthcare professionals at all educational levels and in all practice settings should strive to become politically knowledgeable and actively participate in policy decision making. Mason, Leavitt, and Chaffee (2006) identified four spheres in which nurses can influence policy: government, workplace, organizations, and community (see **Figure** 1). These four spheres can also be applied to other healthcare professionals. These spheres of influence are based on the situational and organizational context in which nurses and healthcare professionals engage in practice. Nurses and some healthcare professionals are employed in government offices and the executive branch. Nurses and healthcare professionals engage in policy development and formulation through their work environment. As professionals, healthcare providers are members of several clinical specialty organizations in addition to organizations of personal interest. As citizens, healthcare professionals are members of communities and in some situations the healthcare professional's workplace is encompassed within the community setting. This sphere of influence model emphasizes the healthcare professional's role in impacting policy based on the multiple contextual situations in which these individuals live and practice. In addition, the healthcare professionals are powerful both in numbers and in the intensity of their commitment to impact policy decision making and policy outcomes. Nurses and other healthcare professionals are encouraged to capitalize on their collective potential to influence policy.

Policy Defined

An understanding of the word *policy* requires comprehension of multiple definitions and the various manners in which the term is used to convey different meanings. The term *policy* can be used to refer to standing decisions or principles that serve as guidelines for actions. It has also been used to refer to proposals, goals, programs, position statements, or opinions of organizations. Therefore, policy has numerous definitions depending on the context and manner of use. Definitions vary from very simple to complex contextual meanings. The following is a brief summary of multiple definitions of *policy*:

- The principles that govern an action directed toward a given outcome
- A way and means of doing things
- A stated position on an issue
- A plan or course of action selected by any branch of the government or organization
- Authoritative statements, decisions, or guidelines that direct individual behavior toward a specific goal
- Authoritative decisions rendered by any branch of government—legislative, judicial, or executive (Longest, 2005; Mc Lean & Mc Millian, 2010; Titmus, 1974)

The multiple definitions of policy indicate that policy is considered a discipline, an entity or an outcome, and a process for achieving a desired outcome. Therefore, the context in which the term *policy* is used must be considered in order to understand the intended meaning. **Table** 1 presents other policy-related terms.

Table 1   Policy Related Terms

Policy solution	The proposed answer that will resolve the expressed issue or problem.
Private policy	Policy not within the public domain that is typically produced by or governing nongovernmental agencies or organizations.
Policy intention	The expected or anticipated outcome. The policy intention represents what is meant to be achieved by the policy.
Unintended consequences	Sometimes known as policy blowback, these are the unexpected effects that result from the politics surrounding a policy or the development and implementation of a policy.
Policy effect	The measurable impact of a policy which can be intended or unintended.

Policy and Political Theory

Theory attempts to describe, explain, and predict behavior and processes. Theories are made up of concepts and constructs that define the theoretical paradigm that facilitates describing, explaining, and predicting behavior and processes. These concepts are linked together through a theoretical framework that identifies propositional statements. These propositions explain the manner in which the theorist perceives the concepts as related. From a policy and political perspective, characteristics of good theory exhibit a valid representation of reality; economy of scale; testability; heuristic nature; prediction simulation; relevance and usefulness; powerful inferences; reliability through replication; objectivity; veracity; and logical organization (Smith & Larimer, 2009).

Types of Policy

There are multiple types of policy. Policy types are designated based on the intent and focus of the policy. Some policy is not mutually exclusive to one typology. For example, some health policy may also be considered public health policy. In addition to the various definitions of policy, there are different types of policy that further contribute to the meaning of the term. The different types of policy are health, public, public health, social, institutional, organizational, and legal. The type and scope of policy that exists is determined by the governmental structure and political and economic systems. These various types of policy are not always mutually exclusive in their defining characteristics.

Health Policy

Health policy can be generated through governments, institutions, or professional associations. Health policy consists of policy that impacts the health of individuals, families, special populations, or communities. Health policy includes policies that affect the production, provision, and financing of healthcare services. Health policy integrates the definition of health and policy. Health is a concept that is accepted as important to individuals and communities. Some definitions of health are rather simplistic, other definitions define health along a continuum. A simplistic definition of health is the mere absence of disease. Other definitions of health recognize health as existing along a continuum that includes maximal states of positive health and recognizes that an illness or disease process may be present but the individual may experience a positive state of being that is interpreted as "healthy." A generally accepted definition of health at both the national and international level is the World Health Organization's (WHO) health definition. The WHO defines health as a state of complete physical, mental, and social well-being and not merely the absence of disease or infirmity (World Health Organization, 1998).

Health policy builds on this basic definition of health. Health policy, in general terms, is any policy that affects the health of individuals, communities, or society. Health policy is considered a broad type of policy that may include other types of policy such as public policy or public health policy.

Public Policy

Public policy is policy that impacts the general public or citizens. It generally serves the interest of the public. Public policies are authoritative statements

4

generated from the three branches of government—executive, legislative, or judicial—that impact the general public. Defining attributes of public policy are made in the "public's" name, made or initiated by a branch of the government, and interpreted or implemented by the public sector. The definitions of public policy are numerous, without consensus on one definition. The following are some accepted public policy definitions:

- Whatever the government chooses to do or not to do to regulate behavior, organize bureaucracies, distribute benefits, or extract taxes (Dye, 2002)
- The sum of government activities that influences the life of citizens, whether the government acts directly or through other agents (Peters, 1999)
- "A statement by the government of what it intends to do or not to do, such as a law, regulation, ruling, decision, or order, or a combination of these" (Birkland, 2001, p. 132)
- Authoritative decisions made by the three branches of government—executive, legislative, or judicial—that are intended to direct or influence the actions, behaviors, or decisions of others (Longest, 2005)

The definitions of public policy vary by author. However, the definitions of public policy do have common elements or themes. These commonalities focus on governmental influence or regulation and governmental action directed toward individuals or communities.

The World Health Organization further defines what is considered healthy public policy. The WHO (1998) considers healthy public policy as any course of action adopted and pursued (by a government, business, or other organization) that can be anticipated to improve (or has improved) health and reduce inequities in health. Public policy is generally considered a product of some public demand that elicits a government-directed course of action aimed at resolving a problem, or in response to political pressure. The distinctive purposes of public policy are to resolve conflict over scarce resources and provide programs that meet public needs.

Public Health Policy

Public health policy intersects policy that is health related but impacts the general population. It may be defined as "the administrative decisions made by the legislative, executive, or judicial branches of government that define courses of action affecting the health of a population through influencing actions, behaviors, or resources" (Porche, 2003, p. 318). This is in contrast to health policies, which are considered applicable only within specific organizations or institutions, known as organizational or institutional health policy.

Social Policy

Social policy consists of policy that impacts the general welfare of the public. Policy that focuses on meeting the human needs of education, housing, and instrumental social support is typically considered a type of social policy. Some exemplars of social policy areas include:

- Unemployment
- Social security
- Housing
- Education
- Food subsidy programs

Institutional Policy

Institutional policies are policies that are developed or implemented by an institution that affects the respective constituents of the institution. Institutional policies frequently govern the workplace environment. Typical institutional policies consist of policies and procedures outlined in operational manuals.

Organizational Policy

Organizational policies are administrative decisions typically made by a board of directors that outline the decisions, position, or official statements that represent the constituents of the organization. Organizational policies can be in the form of bylaws, policy and procedure manuals, articles of incorporation, resolutions, or position statements.

Legal Policy

Legal policy is generally policy founded upon laws or officially accepted rules promulgated through a legislative or executive governmental process. In addition, legal policy does include case law that is developed through judicial opinions and judgments. Legal policy includes policies that relate to the legal profession. Legal policy includes policy that conforms to the law. Most laws are considered policy but not all policy is considered law or legal policy. For example, institutional and organizational policies may or may not consist of laws or legal policy.

Health, public, public health, social, institutional, organizational, or legal types of policy assume many forms. These various types of policies can be in the form of law, rules or regulations, operational decisions, or judicial decisions. Laws can be enacted at all levels of government. Laws are generally considered free standing legislative enactments that attempt to achieve a predetermined outcome. Laws enacted at the federal or state levels of government are implemented through the formation of rules and regulations by agencies within the executive branch of government. In addition to the formation of rules and regulations, executive branch agencies develop programmatic operational decisions that further implement the intent of the law. These operational decisions can be in the form of policies or procedures. Decisions rendered through the judicial branch can also formulate legal policy. Administrative decisions from the judicial branch are precedent setting in the formation of policy, such as with case law.

Another typology of policy is whether it is substantive or procedural. Substantive policy is policy that significantly changes or alters the current status of events. Procedural policy informs the manner or process in which the policymaking body implements changes.

Policy Intention

Policy is developed and formulated with a specific strategic intention. Two strategies that assist with the implementation of the policy intent are regulation and allocation. A policy with a regulatory intent is designed to prescribe and control the behavior of a particular population. A policy with an allocation intent focuses on providing resources in the form of income, services or goods to ensure implementation of policy to individuals or institutions. Allocation policies can be distributive or redistributive. Distributive policy doles out resources in a planned manner consistent with the policy intent. In contrast, redistributive policy redirects existing resources from a current allocation mechanism to a new direction through a different allocation mechanism.

Policymakers

The policy process engages a variety of different individuals and organizations. Individuals who participate in the development and formulation of policy are referred to as policymakers. Policymakers consist of legislators, executive agency employees, and institutional and organizational administrators and leaders. Individuals who are in, or have privileged access to, the inner circle or upper echelon of Congress, the state legislature, executive agencies, or organizational and institutional leadership are referred to as policy elites. In addition, the policymakers themselves are also referred to as policy elites (Buse, Mays, & Walt, 2005).

Networks

Issue networks consist of individuals or coalitions with an active citizen base that is politically interconnected. These issue networks have specialized policy knowledge especially regarding their issue of interest. Issue networks are considered important to policymakers and the policymaking process. Issue networks generally are aligned with the sentiment of the citizens. In addition, issue networks are a resource that has the ability to apply political power and pressure on policymakers and to generate policy solutions (Smith & Larimer, 2009). Sabatier (2007) refers to policy networks that are similar to what Smith and Larimer describe, and characterizes policy networks as stable patterns of social relations between interdependent constituents that form around a problem or policy. Network management provides the ability to impact these policy networks in the manner desired for collective action.

Network management may be considered a political strategy. Network management consists of controlling and organizing constituents with different goals or preferences in relation to a problem or policy alternative into the same existing relationship network or coordinating divergent efforts within an existing network to impact a specific policy. Network management is also the merging of multiple networks into one network for a common purpose or cause. The effectiveness of network management is dependent upon the number of constituents, the critical mass of constituents needed to exert political power, complexity of existing networks, extent of self-reliance of network, dominance of network, and the degree of conflict of interest between network members and the entire network (Sabatier, 2007).

Policy Decision Making: Influencing Factors

The policy decision-making process is influenced by multiple factors. A general systems model has been used to describe the forces that influence the policy decision-making process. Greipp (2002) identified three major forces that affect policy decision making: consumers, providers, and regulatory bodies. Motivating and inhibiting factors were identified that affect the decision-making process.

Consumers are considered clients, families, and communities. Consumer forces are represented by those who have a perceived need for healthcare services and products. Providers are healthcare professionals who render care to clients, and also scientists or researchers. Providers include family caregivers. The last driving force in health policy decision making is regulatory bodies. Regulatory bodies include governments, legal systems, third-party payers, political action committees, other special interest groups, and ethics and institutional review board committees. These three driving forces interact and influence each other during the health policy decision-making process. The factor with the greatest influence will shape the policy issue and policy adopted (Greipp, 2002).

Motivators and inhibitors are the intervening positive and negative variables that can influence the perspective of consumers, providers, or regulatory bodies. Motivators are the positive variables that influence the decision making in the direction of what is best for the common good. Inhibitors are negative variables that influence the perspective in the direction of self interest rather than public interest (Greipp, 2002).

Agenda Setting

One of the first processes of policymaking, is agenda setting. Many believe that agenda setting is the most critical aspect of policy development and formulation. The word "agenda" indicates that there is some type of prioritization of issues or some listing of issues that is defined as relevant or pertinent. Policymakers must be aware of competing and multiple agendas that influence the public and stakeholder opinion regarding policy. There are typically at least four agendas regarding each issue: media agenda, public agenda, political agenda, and the executive branch/government agenda (Prouty, 2000).

Agenda setting is the process of determining what problems are deserving of policy solutions and resolution at the current time. Kingdon's policy development model proposes the interaction of three policy streams that create a window of opportunity when these respective streams align. These three streams are problem, policy, and political (see Chapter 7). An individual who ensures that the respective problem is brought to the policymaking arena is known as a *policy entrepreneur*. A policy entrepreneur seizes the opportunity within a favorable political climate to bring the policy problem to the forefront of the public agenda for policy development (Kingdon, 1995).

An agenda is a collection of problems, understandings of causes, symbols, solutions, and other elements of public concern that attract the attention of members of the public and/or policymakers. An agenda is also referred to as a coherent set of proposals, each related to the other and forming a series of potential enactments. As stated previously, agenda setting is the process by which problems and potential solutions gain or lose attention and potential for policy action. There are multiple levels of agenda. Each agenda level brings the issue or policy closer to the action potential of policymaking. The agenda levels are agenda universe, systemic agenda, institutional agenda, and decision agenda. The agenda universe represents all the ideas that could potentially be brought up and discussed within a society or political system. Systemic agenda represent the issues that are commonly perceived by members of a political group or community as meriting some public attention and involving matters within their scope of authority or legitimate jurisdiction for action. Institutional agenda is a subset of the broader systemic agenda. The institutional agenda represents the items explicitly being given consideration for action by the policymakers. Lastly, the decision agenda contains those items that are actively on the table for policymaking action by policymakers. **Figure** 1 presents a model of the policy agenda levels (Kingdon, 1995). The movement of issues through the various levels of an agenda is influenced by multiple variables.

Agenda setting is influenced by interpersonal social and political networks. These networks exert considerable influence on policy agenda setting. This is sometimes referred to as interpersonal agenda setting. Interpersonal agenda setting uses social or political networks to mediate relationships among involved stakeholders and constituents such as policymakers, governmental representatives, elected officials, media, and the general public, to influence the agenda and ultimately policy.

Other driving forces of agenda setting consist of the problem's magnitude, research, political forces, public opinion, and the government's executive official. Problems that are defined and placed on the policy agenda for policy formulation are generally broadly identified by policymakers as important or requiring urgent action to resolve a public health or safety issue. In addition, the perceived magnitude of a problem can be influenced by the amount of

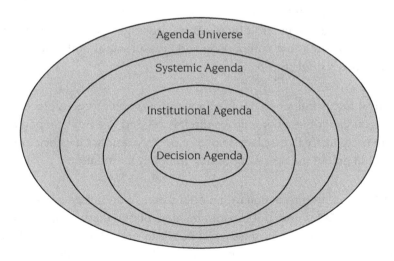

Figure 1   Agenda levels model.

public salience and amount of conflict surrounding the respective problem or policy. Problems that have a broad or widespread implication are more likely to be placed on the policy agenda for policy development and formulation. The placement of a problem on the policy agenda is also dependent upon the social and political context of the circumstances surrounding the problem at the given time (Longest, 2005).

A problem represents an unsettled matter that demands a solution or decision. Two general requisites of a *problem* are a perplexing or vexing situation, and an invitation for a solution. A problem is generally considered an area in which there is a discrepancy between what is wanted (desired situation) and what exists (current situation). Sabatier (2007) proposes that problem analysis consists of examining the participants, positions, outcomes, action-outcome linkages, level of control participant's exercise, information available, and the cost and benefits associated with developing a policy to resolve the problem.

Research data provide support for the policy agenda. Research data, such as epidemiological data, outline the determinants of a problem and proposes the impact of an issue, for example through morbidity and mortality statistics. Research determines the extent and nature of a problem, clarifies the associative or related factors, and provides evaluative data regarding potential policy alternative solutions. Research data clarify the problem for placement on the policy agenda. In addition, research presents data that form the baseline foundation for future comparison and measurement of the policy impact and outcomes (Longest, 2005).

Political forces influence the likelihood of a problem being placed on the policy agenda. Problems or policies directly related to a political party's platform are more likely to be placed on their policy agenda. Chapter 10 provides more detail on the influence of politics on policy formulation.

Public opinion's interaction with media creates a cyclic agenda-setting process. The media informs public opinion, and public readership impacts the media's focus on problems or issues of public interest. Each informs the other within the policy agenda setting process. Public opinion can be shared directly with elected officials, through special interest polls, and communicated with the press through letters to the editor.

The governmental elected officer (e.g., president, governor, or mayor) commands the attention of the public and media. These elected officials frequently communicate to the public through the media. During this communication, they are informing the public using the media as a means to prime and frame the problems. These governmental officers have the ability to communicate in the public domain their expected direction for problem resolution and the proposed policy resolution. Formal forums used to communicate these issues are framed as "State of the State" or "State of the Union" speeches. These speeches frequently outline the respective governmental elected officer's policy agenda (Longest, 2005). The manner in which the problems are outlined and policy resolutions are presented frame our thinking regarding the viable policy options and expected outcomes.

Policy Models

A *model* is a description of a complex entity or processes in an understandable manner. A model is sometimes described as a complex program, process, or entity that is replicable within other similar situations. Models are designed to be summative in nature. A model may be composed of a narrative description with an associated figure detailing the relationships between the concepts, variables, or items represented in the model. A policy model is a description of the complex process of developing, implementing, and evaluating the policies and the policymaking processes within a political sphere of influence. Some policy models are presented in the following material and in Chapter 7. These policy models are used to explain the policymaking process but can also be used as a framework to conduct policy analysis (see Chapter 8).

Hall Agenda Setting Model

The Hall Agenda Setting model proposes that an issue or problem emerges on the policy agenda when three criteria are strongly met. These three criteria are legitimacy, feasibility, and support. Legitimacy of an issue or problem is established if the policymaking body believes they have an obligation to engage. Feasibility represents the potential ability to implement the policy solution. Feasibility is dependent upon the availability of necessary resources, such as knowledge, human, fiscal, and physical. Support refers to the amount of public support for the issue or problem (Buse, Mays, & Walt, 2005).

Policy Triangle Model

The policy triangle model is a simplified approach to understanding the policy making process using four inter-related factors. Buse, Mays, and Walt (2005) propose four factors that define the policy triangle as policy context, policy process, policy content, and actors. The policy context consists of the systemic factors that have an impact on the policy solution. Policy context also consists of situational factors (transient conditions that impact policy), structural factors (unchanging elements of society), cultural factors (value and belief systems), and exogenous factors (level of interdependence or level of sovereignty). The policy process is the systematic process of policymaking (problem identification, policy formulation, policy implementation, and policy evaluation). The policy content consists of the policy resolution. Actors are individuals who engage in the policymaking process such as constituents, interest groups, or legislators (Smith & Larimer, 2009).

Politics, Policy, and Values Model

Policymaking is considered a complex, multidimensional, dynamic process that is influenced by the values of those individuals who establish the policy agenda, determine the policy alternatives, define the goals to be achieved by the policy, the implementation methods, and ultimately the manner in which the policy is evaluated. This model asserts that the value framework of everyone involved provides the large context in which decisions are rendered. Politics is the next contextual sphere that is within the espoused value system and also provides a comprehensive context in which the policymaking process occurs. At the core of the model exist the policymaking stages, which are circular and repetitive. These stages consist of agenda, goals, policy alternatives, policy selection, policy implementation, policy evaluation, then cycling back to agenda setting. Politics influences each step of the process (Mason, Leavitt, & Chaffee, 2006).

"Garbage Can" Model

This model proposes that there are policy solutions that have been previously discarded as possible or applicable that remain circulating with the potential policy sphere. These discarded policy solutions might get attached to an identified policy issue or problem (Hanney, Gonzalez-Block, Buxton, &

Kogan, 2003). This discarded policy solution may or may not be appropriate to the problem or issue but gets attached as a viable solution.

Contextual Model

Policy models provide the framework to understand policy and the policy-making process. The contextual policy model proposes at least five contextual dimensions to define the environment which influences policymaking. This contextual model of policy can also facilitate policy analysis. The five contextual dimensions are:

- Complexity and uncertainty of the decision-system environment
- Potential for constituent feedback
- Ability by constituents to control policy formulation
- Stability of constituents and policymakers over time
- Activation of the interested parties

Schneider and Ingram Social Construction Model

The social construction model emphasizes the role of the target population's influence in policymaking processes. Schneider and Ingram (1993) propose that the policymaking process can best be understood by knowing the legislative official's perception of target populations and their respective needs. They further propose that the target population can be categorized as advantaged, contenders, dependents, or deviants. The manner in which the respective target population is seen and categorized will determine the level of influence the respective group has over policymaking. The social construction model perceives target populations along two dimensions, positive or negative, and powerful or powerless. The target populations are perceived in relation to their relative power base and ability to influence policy. For example, children and disabled persons can be categorized as dependent and are viewed very positively but may be perceived as having less power than other groups.

In addition, Schneider and Ingram propose five categories of tools used to influence the policymaking process. These tools are authority, incentive, capacity-building, symbolic and hortatory, and learning (Schneider & Ingram, 1990). Authority tools are statements substantiated by legitimate forms of governmental power that grant permission or prohibit specific actions in certain circumstances. Incentive tools are motivators that influence an individual to engage in volitional behavior to receive the motivator. Capacity-building tools provide needed education, training, or resources to empower individuals to make decisions or engage in activities. Symbolic and hortatory tools use the individual's internal motivation as a catalyst for action based on their beliefs and values. Learning tools use needs assessment data to identify the informational needs and inform the needed policy.

Political Influence Model

Political influence represents the ability of an individual or group to impact the policy agenda and policy development and formulation process. The political influence model proposes that nurses have the ability to significantly influence policy development, formulation, and implementation within four spheres. The four spheres of influence are government, workplace, organizations, and community. A nurse's active engagement in these environments provides the nurse with an opportunity to advocate for specific policy agendas and influence policy development and formulation from a nursing perspective. Other healthcare professionals as well as nurses can engage in political influence within these four spheres. **Figure** 2 presents visual representation of the political influence model.

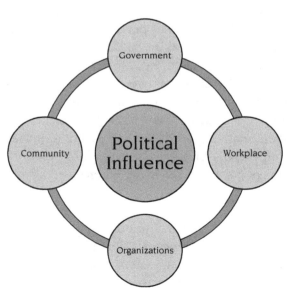

Figure 2 Political influence model.

6 Ps Model

The 6 Ps policy model provides a simplistic framework from which to understand the multiplicative factors that influence policy development. The 6 Ps policy model consists of policy, process, players, politics, press, and public polls. **Figure 3** depicts the aspects of the 6 Ps policy model.

Problem-Centered Public Policymaking Process Model

The problem-centered public policymaking process model presents a complex, dynamic, nonlinear, cyclical, and iterative process that can be used to understand policymaking and to analyze policy. The model is considered to

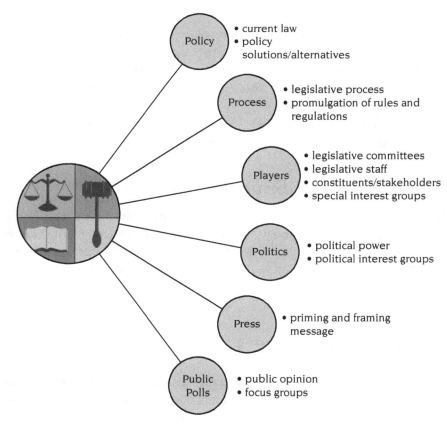

Figure 3 6 Ps policy model.

revolve around a central core element, the problem. A premise of the model is that problem recognition and correct identification of the "real" problem are necessary conditions for the policy-making process. This model considers the major players in the policymaking process to consist of legislators, members of the executive branch, and members of interest groups. This model recognizes that policymaking and policy analysis are two separate processes; however, these activities may occur concurrently as a means to formulate or modify policy. The six phases of the problem-centered public policy-making process are:

- Agenda setting—the initial and crucial phase that uses Kingdon's three streams—problems, policy, and politics to determine the readiness of the window of opportunity to develop policy
- Policy formulation—identifying policy alternatives and developing or formulating the selected policy alternative
- Policy adoption—selection of the policy
- Policy implementation—mobilization of the physical, human, and fiscal resources to carry out the intended policy
- Policy assessment—determining the extent to which the policy implementation is in alignment with the intention, statutory requirements, and expected objectives
- Policy modification—using the policy assessment to modify, maintain, or eliminate the implemented policy (Dunn, 2009)

Punctuated Equilibrium (PE) Model

Punctuated equilibrium describes the process of achieving policy change. This model proposes that policymaking occurs through incremental changes that occur over an extended period of time. These extended periods of incremental policy changes are followed by brief periods of major or transformational policy change (Sabatier, 2007).

Policy Cycle–Process

The formation and implementation of policy experiences revision as findings from policy analysis, policy evaluation, and policy research informs policymakers of needed changes in the current policy. This process is referred to as the policy cycle. The policy cycle is composed of 10 components that are cyclic:

issue raising, agenda setting, policy drafting, public support building, policy-maker support building, policy development and formulation, policy passage, policy implementation, policy evaluation, and policy revision. **Figure** 4 depicts the policy cycle. *Policy* consists of the current laws and policies that are competitive and similar along with all potential policy solutions and alternatives. *Process* includes the legislative processes required to evolve from policy idea to draft policy. Depending on the level of policy development—federal, state, or within an executive agency—the policy process may include the promulgation of rules and regulations in accordance with administrative law and procedures. Players include all individuals and groups that have a vested interest in the problem or policy resolution. Politics consists of the processes utilized to influence the public, legislators, or other stakeholders regarding the

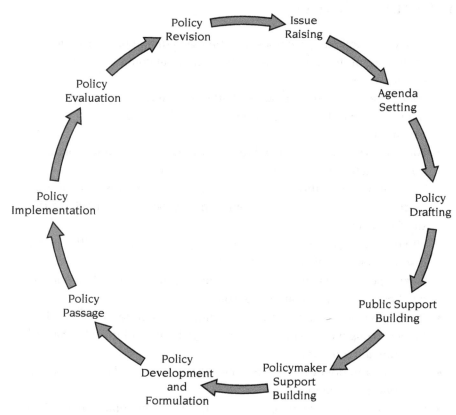

Figure 4 Policy cycle.

desired course of policy action. Press represents the media message regarding the problem or policy resolution. Lastly, public polls provide a real-time assessment of public opinion regarding the proposed policy (Hall-Long, 2009).

Policy on Policy

A policy on policy is a guidance document regarding several aspects of the policymaking process. Policy on policy implies that a policy is generated to outline the terminology used in the policymaking process, the manner in which policies are made, the policy approval process, the time interval for reviewing policies for modification and change, and frequently outlines the policy model for the governmental body, organization, or institution.

Summary Points

- Policy and political processes are strategies that nurses and other healthcare professionals can use to implement community- and societal-level change.
- Four spheres in which nurses and other healthcare professionals can influence policy are government, workplace, organizations, and community.
- The term *policy* has been used to refer to proposals, goals, programs, position statements, or opinions of organizations.
- The multiple definitions of policy indicate that policy is considered a discipline, an entity, or an outcome, and a process of achieving a desired outcome.
- The different types of policy are health, public, public health, social, institutional, organizational, and legal.
- Health policy consists of policy that impacts the health of individuals, families, special populations, or communities.
- Public policies are authoritative statements generated from the three branches of government—executive, legislative, or judicial—that impact the general public.
- Public health policy intersects policy that is health related but impacts the general population.
- Social policy consists of policy that impacts the general welfare of the public.

- Institutional policies are policies that are developed or implemented by an institution that affects the respective constituents of the institution.
- Organizational policies are administrative decisions typically made by a board of directors that outlines the decisions, position, or official statements that represent the constituents of the organization.
- Legal policy is generally policy that is founded upon laws or officially accepted rules promulgated through a legislative or executive governmental process.
- Most laws are considered policy but not all policy is considered law or legal policy.
- A policy with an allocation intent focuses on providing resources in the form of income, services, or goods to ensure implementation of policy to individuals or institutions.
- Distributive policies dole out resources in a planned manner consistent with the policy intent.
- Issue networks consist of individuals or coalitions with an active citizen base that is politically interconnected.
- Network management consists of controlling and organizing constituents with different goals or preferences in relation to a problem or policy alternative into the same existing relationship network or coordinating divergent efforts within an existing network to impact a specific policy.
- Individuals who are in, or have privileged access to, the inner circle or upper echelon of Congress, the state legislature, executive agencies, or organizational and institutional leadership are referred to as policy elites.
- Three major forces that affect policy decision making are consumers, providers, and regulatory bodies.
- There are typically at least four agendas regarding each issue: media agenda, public agenda, political agenda, and the executive branch/ government agenda.
- Agenda setting is the process of determining what problems are deserving of policy solutions and resolution at the current time.
- Kingdon's policy development model proposes the interaction of three policy streams that create a window of opportunity when these respective streams align. These three streams are problems, policy, and politics.

- Agenda setting is influenced by interpersonal social and political networks.
- Policymaking is considered a complex, multidimensional, dynamic process that is influenced by the values of those individuals who establish the policy agenda, determine the policy alternatives, define the goals to be achieved by the policy, the implementation methods, and ultimately the manner in which the policy is evaluated.
- The six phases of the problem-centered public policy-making process are: agenda setting, policy formulation, policy adoption, policy implementation, policy assessment, and policy modification.
- The policy cycle is composed of 10 components that are cyclic: issue raising, agenda setting, policy drafting, public support building, policymaker support building, policy development and formulation, policy passage, policy implementation, policy evaluation, and policy revision.
- Policy on policy is a guidance document to the entire policymaking process for a governmental body or organization.

References

Birkland, T. (2001). *An introduction to the policy process: Theories, concepts, and models of public policy making*. Armonk, NY: M. E. Sharpe.

Bobrow, D., & Dryzek, J. (1987). *Policy analysis by design*. Pittsburgh, PA: University of Pittsburgh Press.

Buse, K., Mays, N., & Walt, G. (2005). *Making health policy*. Berkshire, UK: Open University Press.

Dunn, W. (2009). *Public policy analysis: An introduction* (4th ed.). Englewood Cliffs, NJ: Prentice Hall.

Dye, T. (2010). *Understanding public policy* (13th ed.). Upper Saddle River, NJ: Prentice Hall.

Greipp, M. (2002). Forces driving health care policy decisions. *Policy, Politics and Nursing*, 3(1), 35–42.

Hall-Long, B. (2009). Nursing and public policy: A tool for excellence in education, practice, and research. *Nursing Outlook*, 57, 78–83.

Hanney, S., Gonzalez-Block, M., Buxton, M., & Kogan, M. (2003). The utilization of health research in policy-making: Concepts, examples and methods of assessment. *Health Research Policy and Systems*, 1(2), 1–28.

Kingdon, J. (1995). *Agendas, alternatives, and public policies* (2nd ed.). New York, NY: Longman.

Longest, B. (2005). *Health policymaking in the United States* (4th ed.). Washington, DC: Association of University Programs in Health Administration.

Mason, D., Leavitt, J., & Chaffee, M. (2006). *Policy and politics in nursing and health care* (5th ed.). St. Louis, MO: Saunders.

Porche, D. (2003). *Public & community health nursing practice: A population-based approach.* Thousand Oaks, CA: Sage.

McLean, I., & McMillan, A. (2010). *The concise Oxford dictionary of politics* (3rd ed.). Oxford, England: Oxford University Press.

Peters, B. G. (1999). *American public policy: Promise and performance.* Chatham, NJ: Chatham House Publishers.

Prouty, J. (2000). *Agenda setting function of Maxwell McCombs & Donald Shaw.* Retrieved from http://oak.cats.ohiou.edu/~jp340497/agsapp.htm

Sabatier, P. (2007). *Theories of the policy process* (2nd ed.). Boulder, CO: Westview Press.

Schneider, A., & Ingram, H. (1993). Social construction of target populations: Implications for politics and policy. *American Political Science Review, 87*(2), 334–347.

Schneider, A., & Ingram, H. (1990). Behavioral assumptions of policy tools. *Journal of Politics, 52*(2), 510–529.

Smith, K., & Larimer, C. (2009). *The public policy theory primer.* Boulder, CO: Westview Press.

Titmus, R. (1974). *Social policy: An introduction.* New York, NY: Pantheon.

World Health Organization. (1988). *Adelaide recommendations on healthy public policy.* Retrieved from http://www.who.int/hpr/NPH/docs/AdelaideRecommendations.pdf

World Health Organization. (1998). *Health promotion glossary.* Retrieved from http://www.who.int/hpr/NPH/docs/hp_glossary_en.pdf

Government Response: Legislation

Politics: Playing the Game

Janice Kay Lanier

"Politics is the art of problem solving."

—Jonah Goldberg, Editor-at-Large, *National Review Online*

KEY TERMS

Constituents: Residents of a geographic area who can vote for a candidate and whom the elected official represents.

Interest group: An organized group with a common cause that works to influence the outcome of laws, regulations, or programs.

Lobbyist: An individual who works to influence legislators and other governmental decision makers.

Political action committee (PAC): A formal organization that exists to engage in a process through which candidates for political office are endorsed and otherwise supported. It must adhere to state and/or federal laws in carrying out its activities.

INTRODUCTION

For many nurses, "politics" is a dirty word; it is the seamy side of the policymaking process that they prefer to ignore. Unfortunately, participating in the political aspects of policymaking is not an optional exercise. In many respects, such participation is key to ensuring nurses have a place at the policy table. Before one can influence policy, one has to be in the room where policy is being debated and developed—policy is made by those who show up, not necessarily by people with special expertise, and the usual way into the room is through the door labeled "political participation and savvy." Even nurses who do see the need for political participation are somewhat naïve as to exactly what that participation entails and how to do it effectively. In part, it means playing the political game by the rules—even distasteful rules—at least until nurses have sufficient presence and clout to be able to affect the rules themselves. This chapter is intended to provide insight into the subtle rules governing political participation and set out the options available to nurses for finding their way through the political maze.

POLITICAL INVOLVEMENT: OPTION VERSUS OBLIGATION

"If you're not at the table, you're on the menu."

—SUSAN CLARK, RN, LOBBYIST (PATTERSON, 2011, P. 1)

Nurses are part of a regulated profession in a regulated industry. One cannot become a nurse without meeting the requirements set forth in state laws. These laws contain the statutory definition of nursing practice; licensure requirements and exceptions to those requirements; grounds for discipline and penalties for violating the law; and numerous other provisions. Once one meets the requirements to be called a registered nurse or advanced practice nurse, the law (both state and federal) goes on to define payment mechanisms, establish staffing expectations, identify acceptable professional relationships, etc. These laws, which permeate the practice of nursing and health care in general, are made in political arenas in Washington, D.C., and in state legislatures across the country.

Despite the key role of the political process in their professional lives, most nurses characterize political activism as something for others to do. Politics somehow seems far removed from their everyday reality or experience and is seen as something that interferes with what is really important—caring for patients safely and effectively. Although many nurses decry political involvement, in reality, it is not an option, but a professional obligation. In other words, some level of political participation and political savvy are just as crucial to a nurse's practice as knowledge of pharmacology, physiology, and psychology.

Not surprisingly, nurses' attitudes with respect to political participation have hampered the profession's ability to be viewed by key policymakers as a powerful political force, even in matters dealing with healthcare reform. "Nurses don't show up" is the phrase used by many legislators to describe nurses' participation in the legislative process. Interestingly, the general public believes that nurses and nursing's interests were underrepresented when healthcare reform was debated in Washington in 2009. Nurses no doubt agree with the public's assertion; however, agreeing alone does not ensure a greater role for nurses in future debates. To secure a meaningful place at the policy table, nurses will have to embrace their profession's political side and make the politically-savvy nurse the rule rather than the exception.

Documents setting out professional obligations and expectations for nurses unequivocally agree on the importance of political participation. *Nursing's Social Policy Statement* includes in the elements of the profession's social contract the following statements:

- Public policy and the health care delivery system influence the health and well-being of society and professional nursing.
- Individual responsibility and inter-professional involvement are essential (American Nurses Association, 2010, p. 7).

The statement identifies one of the essential features of professional nursing as the "influence on social and public policy to promote social justice" (p. 9). The *Code of Ethics for Nurses* (American Nurses Association, 2010) alludes throughout to the role nurses play in promoting, advocating, and striving to protect the health, safety, and rights of the patient. This responsibility is not limited to the immediate surroundings in which nursing care is provided, but extends to statehouses, boardrooms, and other arenas in which this advocacy can affect public policy relative to health care and, ultimately, patient outcomes.

Finally, the *Future of Nursing* report issued by the Institute of Medicine in 2010 states that "nurses should be full partners with physicians and other healthcare professionals, in redesigning health care in the United States" (p. S-3). This role will be played out, in part, in the health policy context where nurses should participate in, and sometimes lead, decision-making and be engaged in healthcare reform-related implementation efforts. To be ready to assume this responsibility, nurse education programs should include course content addressing leadership-related competencies for all nurses. These competencies include a firm grounding in politics and policy-making processes.

POLITICS—WHAT IS IT REALLY?

"Politics in a real sense is the people who take the time to participate."

—SEN. DANIEL INOUYE (D-HI)

What is politics? "Politics is a process that includes not only that which is typically associated with political functions (e.g., government, police, workers' unions), but also that which is involved in the regulation, structure, and action of all individuals' behavior" (O'Bryne & Holmes, 2009, p. 155). As political scientists have noted, politics underlies the process through which groups of people make decisions. It is the basis for the authoritative allocation of value. When someone or something has the power to hand out things that are desirable, who gets what, when, and how is determined by politics. In order to be a beneficiary of this largess, people must successfully jump into the political fray.

Although politics is generally associated with behaviors and interactions within civil governments, the essence of politics is applicable to other group relationships—social relations involving authority and power, or methods and tactics used to formulate and apply policy. As long-time U.S. Senator Daniel Inouye (D-HI) acknowledged, "Politics . . . is the people who take time to participate" (Lanier, 1985, p. 166). When one "plays politics," one is considered to be shrewd or prudent in practical matters, tactful, and diplomatic; playing politics is also seen as being contrived in a shrewd and practical way, or being expedient.

There is nothing particularly sinister about these descriptions; however, when one probes current popular electronic sources, the less positive aspects of the political process surface. Linking words such as "intrigue" and "control" to "political power" and governmental functions subtly sends a message that there is something unsavory about politics. When one plays politics, one engages in political intrigue to take advantage of a situation or issue; exploits an option or relationship; and/or deals with people in an opportunistic, manipulative, or devious way. These latter perceptions are what cause politics to be seen as one of the less savory societal activities that many people (especially nurses) go out of their way to avoid.

Nursing practice itself has many tasks or activities associated with it that are seen as distasteful by the general public. Once nurses accept the premise that political participation is as integral to everyday practice as other nursing-related tasks, they should simply don their protective gear and wade in! Before doing so, however, a bit of preparation is warranted.

Putting Politics in Perspective

Although the number of men in nursing has increased over the years (comprising approximately 6–7% of the total number of registered nurses [American Association of Colleges of Nursing, 2011]), the vast majority of nurses continue to be women. Women's struggle to achieve a place at the policymaking table has evolved and parallels the societal changes affecting women as a whole. Going from a largely subordinate role in a patriarchal society to prominent leadership roles in boardrooms (Lanier, 1985), women are now faced with more career choices than ever before. With that transition has come increased opportunities to fill power positions in the workplace and a more powerful presence overall. The suffrage movement in the 20th century gave women the right to vote, and a certain amount of attendant power outside of the workplace came along with that right. Whether women have made the most of that power over the years is debatable; however, political parties recently have become very aware of the importance of the women's vote and are making concerted efforts to win it. Because nursing remains largely a woman's profession, the forces affecting women are the same ones that affect how nurses will be received (and succeed) in the political arena.

With the economic down turn of the early 21st century, health care became one of the few growth industries in the bleak economy. Health care also re-emerged as the focus for one of the most significant policy debates facing the United States. Because of the financial stake state and federal governments have in health care, and the vast investment special interest groups have in the healthcare system, the reform efforts and attendant policymaking took on political overtones from the outset.

Politics and power go hand-in-hand. It's all about power relationships. Interestingly, the concept of "power" is changing as technology has flattened the world and lessened the importance of the traditional trappings of power—money, name, and job title. Despite these changes, power and the perceptions associated with it control political processes and outcomes. While the source of that power may vary, its essence does not.

Power does not exist in a vacuum. Every aspect of power implies a relationship between two or more people. There are varying degrees of power. Simply because someone is powerful in one situation does not mean that power translates to a different venue. Power takes on several forms—coercion, persuasion, and manipulation. Coercion depends on force for its effectiveness, persuasion involves the acceptance of positions put forth by one person without threats, and manipulation is the con man form of power. One can have power because of the position held or because of a special expertise that is needed in a particular situation. The amount or type of resources at one's disposal can determine how much power can be exerted and how that power will affect the relevant political relationships

Nurses most often use persuasion (or perhaps manipulation) rather than coercion to achieve their desired goals. To be an effective persuader, a certain amount of expertise is required not only with respect to the complex issues at hand, but also with respect to the processes and dynamics—the politics—that are at play. In the traditional context in which playing politics is seen as a means to manipulate governmental decisions, a fundamental understanding of the legislative process is important in order to wield or grasp a modicum of power. In other words, there is no substitute for expertise.

Passage of the Affordable Care Act in 2010 was only the beginning of what promises to be an ongoing debate that will affect the future of the nursing profession, as well as health care itself, in the years ahead. Who actually benefits is also the root of healthcare reform debates. Logically, nurses, by virtue of their numbers alone (making up the largest segment of the healthcare workforce), should have the potential to influence the far-reaching policy changes affecting health care; however, the extent of that influence has yet to be measured, and it will happen only if nurses are genuine payers in the political game. The public is certainly supportive of an increased role for nurses in these discussions and debates, thus giving nurses a power base from which to build. However, nurses, especially advanced practice nurses, must first seize the moment and take advantage of the unprecedented opportunities open to them.

Wading In: What Does It Look Like?

"There are two things one should never watch being made—sausage and laws."

—ANONYMOUS

The tools of the legislative process include know-how, networks, and money. Know-how means one must be familiar with both the political processes and the people who are the actors on the political stage, but sadly, the majority of people cannot identify their federal, state, or local elected officials. While many can name the President of the United States, few will be able to say with assurance who represents them in the halls of Congress and fewer still can name their state senators or representatives. Effectiveness in the world of politics is not possible unless one knows who is in the game. Technology has made it easy to learn the identity of lawmakers at every level by simply going to federal or state websites and entering zip code data. These sites also provide brief biographical information, photos, and other pertinent and helpful background material.

Why is this important? Politics is at heart a people process and, like other people-centered endeavors, the relationships among and between people determine outcomes. Nurses are well aware of how important communication and personal connections are in the care-giving context, and those same principles also affect the world of politics. Knowing a state representative and being able to recognize him or her on sight, while also knowing something about the issues, are fundamental to producing solid relationships. Just as nurses realize the importance of establishing good rapport with clients, that same principle applies when establishing the connections needed to influence lawmakers.

In addition to knowing the people, one must also know the process—how laws are made. Most nurses complete a government course in high school and promptly disregard most of the subject matter because it holds little relevance for them at the time. While diagrams depicting "How a Bill Becomes a Law" are important, they are also very rudimentary (see **Figure   1**). There is much more to the process than can be neatly depicted on a chart.

Anatomy of Congress: There are 535 members: 100 senators (two from each state) and 435 House members. The party in control of the majority of seats holds considerable power:

- Setting legislative agenda
- Chairing all committees
- Identifying problems
- Identifying possible solutions that are more likely to be enacted

Each state will follow a similar pattern—two chambers, a senate, and a house (except in Nebraska where there is a unicameral system).

Bills are ideas that legislators have determined need to be ratified into law. The ideas can come from many sources: the legislator's own experiences, the issues brought forward by **constituents**, or by special **interest groups**. Once the idea is drafted into the proper bill format, it is introduced into the House or Senate, depending on the chamber to which the bill's chief sponsor belongs. (All budget bills are initiated in the House, as it was designed to be most representative of the average citizens' interests. Because of the importance of budgeting in regards to policymaking, it was given a primary role in the budget process.)

Once introduced, a bill is then referred to a standing committee for further consideration. These standing committees are generally subject-matter focused, so bills

Figure 1 How a bill passes through Congress.

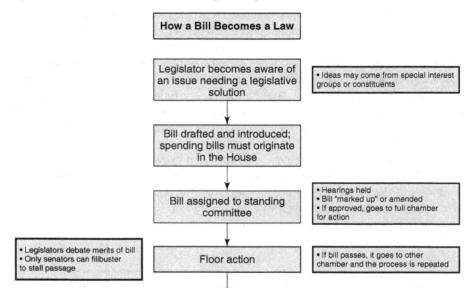

How a Bill Becomes a Law

Legislator becomes aware of an issue needing a legislative solution
- Ideas may come from special interest groups or constituents

Bill drafted and introduced; spending bills must originate in the House

Bill assigned to standing committee
- Hearings held
- Bill "marked up" or amended
- If approved, goes to full chamber for action

- Legislators debate merits of bill
- Only senators can filibuster to stall passage

Floor action
- If bill passes, it goes to other chamber and the process is repeated

Conference committee
- Differences between Senate- and House-passed versions resolved

- If vetoed, goes back to Congress for possible override

Presidential action
- To override veto, need 2/3 majority in both chambers

related to health care go to a health committee, finance issues to a banking committee, farm-related matters to the agriculture committee, and so on. Standing committees can be configured differently over time and subcommittees may be named to consider particular bills in greater detail. Committee hearings are important, but they often appear to be more chaotic than productive. Much of the real business of law making is conducted behind the scenes, but one must also participate in the defined processes to earn a place at the more informal behind-the-scenes-tables.

Committee chairs are extremely influential, particularly with respect to the subject matter areas that are the focus of the committee's work. Chairs determine what bills will be heard and when, and they establish the procedural framework under which the committee operates. The chair's position on an issue can determine its fate from the outset. Because of the extent of their power and influence, committee chairs are able to raise large sums of money from special interest groups to support their re-election, and re-election is always an important consideration for lawmakers. House and Senate leadership (elected by their colleagues) determine who will be named as committee chairs. Certain committees are seen as more prestigious than others, so being named the chair of one of those committees is even more important to an ambitious legislator. Not surprisingly, political considerations play a role in this entire process. Being aware of the dynamics that are the foundation of the overall committee process helps ensure more effective representation by those who want to influence the outcome of the committee's work.

If a bill is able to garner committee approval, it goes to the full chamber for a vote. The timing for scheduling a vote, as well as various attempts to amend the bill or delay the vote, are all integral parts of the lawmaking process. Much maneuvering occurs backstage and the ability to influence these less public interactions is as important as the words or concepts being debated. Again, peoples' relationships and politics determine the ultimate results. To be able to be effective in one's efforts to influence outcomes, one must be aware of these relationships and take them into account. Once a bill is approved in either the House or Senate, it must begin the process again in the other chamber. The chief executive (president or governor) must sign the bill before it can become law and all of this must happen within a single legislative cycle—two years. It is not surprising that it often takes several years for a particular legislative issue to finally become law, especially when the issue is not one that garners a lot of public interest or attention. The state and federal processes each have special nuances, but the overall process is similar for both, as are the people dynamics that affect each step of the process.

Given all the hidden factors that affect success on Capitol Hill or in state legislatures, how can an individual nurse hope to have sufficient knowledge or time to make a difference in the policymaking aspects of the profession? Fortunately, the American Nurses Association (ANA) and its state constituent associations, as well as specialty nursing groups, can provide their members with the tools they need to be successful. The success of these organizations' efforts in the legislative arena depends in large part on their members' involvement with and understanding the importance of an effective legislative presence on behalf of the profession in Washington, D.C., and in statehouses across the country. An individual nurse need only become a member of his/her professional association and then take advantage of the resources provided by these organizations to be part of the cadre of politically-active nurses who are taking seriously the obligations set forth in the profession's social policy statement and its code of ethics. These organizations keep nurses informed about what, why, and how things are happening, as well as help develop succinct messages to be conveyed to key lawmakers.

EFFECTIVE LOBBYING: A THREE-LEGGED STOOL

In addition to knowing the procedural aspects of lawmaking, nurses can also benefit from understanding the lesser known but equally important relational aspects of the process: the connections not depicted on any chart purporting to show how a bill becomes a law. Success in the legislative arena is much like a three-legged stool, with each leg essential to the sturdiness of the stool as a whole. The first leg is the formal lobbying effort provided by independent paid individuals, many of whom have close ties with elected and appointed officials. Leg number two is the grassroots leg, and the third leg is the political leg—the one that actively tries to influence the outcome of elections.

Leg One: Professional Lobbyists

No bill becomes law without lobbyists' input. Lobbying is the act of influencing—the art of persuading—a governmental entity to achieve a specific legislative or regulatory outcome. While anyone can lobby, **lobbyists** are most often individuals who represent special interest groups and are looked to as the experts by lawmakers who need information and rationale for supporting or not supporting a particular issue. The role of lobbyists has become even more critical as the complexity of legislation has increased; for example, the 1914 law creating the Federal Trade Commission was a total of eight pages, the Social Security Act of 1935 totaled 28 pages, and the Financial Reform bill (conference version) of 2010 contained 2,319 pages (Brill, 2010). Legislators, often pressed for time, rely on lobbyists' expertise to help them understand what they are voting for or against.

> *On September 18, 1793, President George Washington laid the cornerstone for the U.S. Capitol. While the shovel, trowel, and marble gavel used for the ceremony are still displayed, repeated efforts to locate the cornerstone itself have been unsuccessful.*
>
> *At times, policymaking seems as shrouded in mystery as the location of the Capitol's cornerstone. That's why you need an experienced partner (a.k.a. lobbyist) to help you unravel the mystery.*
>
> —A pitch for Capitol Tax Partners, a lobbying firm

According to the Center for Responsive Politics, there were 10,404 federal lobbyists in 1998; in 2010, there were 12,488. While this number represents a decrease from a high of 14,869 in 2007, the number of lobbyists has significantly increased over the years. In 1998, $1.44 billion was spent on lobbying; in 2010, the total was $2.61 billion, again down from $3.49 billion spent in 2009. Nevertheless, this represents a general increase overall. The American Nurses Association reported spending $1,197,342 on its lobbying efforts, utilizing the services of six lobbyists. The American Hospital Association, on the other hand, spent $13,585,000 and employed 72 lobbyists, many of whom were categorized as "revolving door" lobbyists, or individuals who left positions in the legislative or regulatory arenas for typically more lucrative private sector employment. (The revolving door provides an entry and connections that are invaluable to a lobbyist and the special interests he/she represents. The more revolving door lobbyists an organization employs, the better connected it is to the inner workings of Capitol Hill.)

The willingness of entities to invest the level of resources associated with lobbying efforts is indicative of how important the connections forged by lobbyists are to the reputations of the interest groups, and to their ability to get the job done. Members of special interest groups expect legislative success, and that success comes with a price. Tellingly, it is a price many nurses are reluctant to embrace. Nurses must be more aware of the key role that lobbyists play and be willing to support the lobbying efforts of professional associations by becoming members of these organizations. Success in the halls of Congress and at statehouses is integral to the advancement of the profession itself and its societal values. Nurses want their legislative agenda advanced successfully, and that expectation comes with a price tag that only nurses can pay.

Leg Two: Grassroots Lobbyists

While the paid lobbyists are the ones who most commonly come to mind when thinking of lobbying efforts, the so-called grassroots lobbying can be more effective if appropriately organized and informed. Grassroots lobbyists are constituents who have the power to elect officials through their vote. When constituents have expertise and knowledge about a particular issue (such as nurses in the healthcare reform debates), they are especially valuable resources for their elected officials. While issues debated in Washington, D.C., are national in scope, members of Congress are still concerned about how the issue is perceived back home. The connections established by a nurse constituent with his/her lawmakers at the federal, state, and local levels may provide timely access and a listening ear at key points during the policymaking process. To be effective, grassroots lobbyists must recognize that getting a law passed can take many years and entails compromise and commitment, along with an understanding of the political forces at work. In addition to employing paid lobbyists, professional nurse organizations have become increasingly aware of the strength of grassroots lobbying—seen by some as the most effective of all lobbying efforts (deVries & Vanderbilt, 1992).

Many state-level associations have established legislative liaison programs that match legislators with a nurse constituent from their districts, then provide nurses the tools needed to become an effective resource for the legislator. The American Nurses Association has also initiated similar efforts, as have other specialty nursing organizations at the federal level. These kinds of relationships take time to develop, but they provide both tangible and intangible benefits if diligently nurtured. An individual nurse who is willing to serve in a liaison capacity can markedly increase a legislator's understanding of nursing and the role nurses play in health care. With increased understanding, the legislator is more apt to be supportive of the profession's legislative agenda.

Before embarking on a lobbying effort, it is important to be aware of ethics laws as they relate to lobbying. Most states have strict reporting requirements, along with restrictions that apply to the use of funds and gifts to influence legislators. These laws generally are targeted at the paid lobbyists rather than grassroots efforts, but because each state defines "lobbying" differently when determining when the ethics laws apply, it is important to review the relevant statutes so as to avoid unwanted surprises later. State nurses associations can provide guidance on this matter.

There is no substitute for visibility in the legislative arena. Showing up is what political activism is all about, and showing up is the essence of lobbying. Building trusting relationships, demonstrating interest and concern for the public good, and providing information on issues important to the nursing profession are all things that can be done through regular participation in all aspects of the legislative process. Grassroots lobbying has been described by some as a "contact sport" (Patterson, 2011, p. 1), with the contacts taking various forms, such as in-person visits (the most effective), personally written letters, fax messages, phone calls, and emails.

Grassroots initiatives can put additional pressure on lawmakers if done well; however, it is not without its risks. Promising to unleash a firestorm of support or opposition to a measure is only effective if the people making up the grassroots actually respond. Promising and not delivering a grassroots campaign affects credibility and actually weakens the interest group's overall influence. When the grassroots response is a message that is repeated verbatim (as with form letters or computerized email messages), it becomes clear that the effort is not a spontaneous outpouring of individuals' sentiments and, therefore, is not the most effective approach. Volume does matter—legislators will ask how many letters or phone calls have been received either supporting or opposing the particular issue—but the best communication includes at least something about the writer's personal experiences with the matter being legislated.

Effective communication tips:

Written:

- Communication should be typed, no longer than two pages and addressing no more than two issues.
- State the purpose of the communication at the beginning.
- Present clear, compelling rationale for the position(s) being advocated.

- When expressing disappointment about a past vote or position, do so respectfully.

Verbal:

- Identify up front the amount of time allocated for the meeting.
- Avoid too much small talk that eats up the allotted time, but take advantage of any shared connections or experiences that might enhance rapport.
- Time should be structured so that the issue can be presented succinctly.
- Do not assume the legislator or aide has the same amount of expertise as you do on the subject, and do not get too complex in your explanations.
- Provide a one-page summary at the end that highlights key points.
- Always send a follow-up note or letter after a meeting, thanking the legislator and/or aide for speaking with you. Always reiterate the points you made during the discussion.

While most people think of lawmaking when considering how policy is made, regulation and rule making are equally important to nursing's agenda. Regulations are made by executive branch agencies in accordance with the somewhat complex administrative procedures acts passed by lawmakers. While the processes vary from state to state, the relationship considerations apply equally to the enactment of laws and the adoption of regulations. One must know the process and the people and establish a reputation as a trustworthy, reliable resource in order to be an effective voice for the profession.

The relationships at issue are not limited to elected officials. Rather, a savvy lobbyist—whether professional or grassroots—knows the value of establishing connections with staff members and legislative aides working for lawmakers, as well as with other lobbyists from various special interest groups. These latter relationships frequently can be more important than direct contact with the legislators themselves. Timing is often the key to success, and having a timely "heads-up" about what is transpiring behind the scenes can mean the difference between success and failure. The connections with staff and other lobbyists are frequently the source for the kinds of tips and gossip that define and redefine strategies for advancing one's agenda.

No lawmaker can be an expert on every issue; therefore, they have grown increasingly reliant on professional staff members to serve as their eyes, ears, and often spokespersons. This is true for state legislators as well. Staff members frequently have political/constituent ties to the legislator.

Congressional staff members include:

- Chief of staff or administrative assistant with oversight responsibilities
- Legislative directors responsible for day-to-day legislative activities
- Press secretary
- Legislative assistants (LAs) who are responsible for specific legislative issues. For example, the health LA may also work on education and Social Security issues. LAs are very influential because of the role they play in the lawmaker's daily activities. The LA may "staff" the congressperson at committee hearings and prepare the member's statements and questions for witnesses. They accompany the legislator to meetings with lobbyists and constituents and are often the gatekeepers who funnel information and opinions. The LA also works with the office called the Legislative Council to draft bill language that includes the policy concepts identified by the lawmaker. The LA is someone a nurse should cultivate and work through.

Committee staff: These individuals support the work of congressional committees. Separate staff members are allocated to the majority and minority parties, with a larger number serving the majority party. Committee staff members have a narrower focus than the legislator's personal staff and are typically older and more experienced. Their duties include:

- Planning committee agendas
- Coordinating hearing schedules and witnesses
- Preparing legislation for committee and floor action
- Gathering and analyzing data
- Drafting committee reports
- Working cooperatively with their counterparts in the other chamber

It is best not to wait until there is an important bill pending to begin developing relationships. Regular contact with legislator offices and staff members to convey interest in the activities and issues they are dealing with and volunteering to serve on committees and task forces can help to develop name recognition, credibility, and trust.

A successful lobbying initiative depends on several additional relational components that are particularly relevant to nurses:

- *Unity:* Divisiveness within the profession is a certain road to defeat and fuels the opposition's fire. Opponents are well aware of the potential impact a united nursing profession could have on health policy decisions and other important issues. Nurse's numbers alone are formidable. For that reason, competing interests subtly and purposefully poke at the hot spots that typically divide nurses (e.g., educational preparation; union vs. non-union). Nurses often align themselves within specialty practice groups and are willing to lobby only when an issue relevant to that particular group is being considered. Ideally, all nurses should have a basic understanding or awareness of the legislative initiatives of specialty groups. They should actively support the initiatives of their colleagues, or, at a minimum, refrain from opposing the cause publicly; instead, concerns should be shared privately in hopes of working towards a compromise position.
- *Outreach:* Nurses have often been too insular in devising legislative strategies. Instead they should seek and define bases of support external to the profession. Identify groups and individuals who have something to gain if the cause is successful or something to lose if it is not. Groups may include consumers, other licensed professionals, and special interest groups such as AARP.
- *Timing:* There are windows of opportunity for a political agenda to move forward. Sometimes it is important to wait for the right climate or the right moment to proceed. Nurses often become impatient when their well-meaning advocacy, which often is intended to improve the public's health, seems to fall on deaf ears. Patience and timing are essential to success. Because of the critical nature of timing, it is often important to be ready to respond at a moment's notice. It is also important to be aware of the general environment in which an issue is being considered. For example, when a state is facing significant budget shortfalls or the nation is headed towards unfathomable deficits, it would not be a good time to try to move a costly program forward without identifying a credible, sustainable funding stream. During periods of reform, there is a stronger likelihood that change can be made.

The legislative process is an evolving one, founded on compromise. Settling for part of an initiative may be the best way to eventually achieve the entire goal. Willingness to persevere and keep returning to the legislature year after year, if necessary, is essential. New faces are chosen at each election and the volatility of the entire political arena can result in major philosophical changes in a relatively short time.

Leg Three: The Role of Money

The final leg of the stool is the one that causes much discomfort and concern to nurses and others: money. Politics in its most primitive form is on display when considering how money influences who wins or loses an election. The amount of money that flows to and through the legislative process has raised serious questions as to whether the whole process is "For Sale" to whoever has the deepest pockets. Unfortunately, winning an election or re-election, even at the local level, can be a very expensive proposition costing millions of dollars. The total spending by political parties, candidates, and issue groups for the mid-term elections in 2010 is estimated to have exceeded $4 billion—a trend that is likely to continue in light of the recent United States Supreme Court decision in *Citizens United v. Federal Election Commission* (2010).

Not only has the amount of money flowing to campaigns increased dramatically, the source of those dollars (who has the deep pockets) has also changed and is expected to change even more in the future. For example, American Crossroads GPS (the brainchild of Republican strategists Karl Rove and Ed Gillespie, both of whom held influential staff positions under former President George W. Bush), American Action Network, Republican Governors Association, and the Chamber of Commerce are groups based in Washington, D.C., that financed state races across the country on behalf of Republican interests in 2010. On the Democratic side, organized labor, EMILY's List, and the League of Conservation Voters continue to contribute millions to fund campaign messages (Crowley, 2010). While these groups may appear to operate independently of each other, in actuality "coordination is as easy as walking across the hall" of their shared office space (p. 31). How this evolving dynamic will affect future elections and alliances remains to be seen, but its existence cannot be ignored or under estimated.

> The Court in its *Citizens United* ruling struck down the 2002 federal campaign finance law prohibiting unions and corporations from spending money directly advocating for or against candidates. The First Amendment was the basis for the Court's decision. The League of Women Voters has voiced its support of legislation that would require disclosure of the sources of the spending that is now legal and basically unlimited as long as the efforts are not coordinated with an individual's campaign.

The need to raise the kind of money in question often discourages potential candidates and gives greater influence to special interest groups that are able to generate large sums of money from members and supporters. Re-election is essential to maintaining incumbency and the opportunity to continue to affect policymaking; therefore, re-election considerations become important almost as soon as the oath of office is administered. Raising money is a year-round expectation, with political party leaders putting pressure on their ranks to meet ambitious fundraising goals. Success in these endeavors often determines who will be elected to leadership positions in the House and Senate and appointed as committee chairs. Incumbents have a significant edge in the fundraising race, which further disadvantages newcomers and ultimately affects election results. For example, in the 2008 election, the odds of a challenger beating an incumbent if the challenger spent under $1 million were 302:1. If the challenger were able to spend $2 million or more the odds changed to 14:9. Contrast that to the 1998 election cycle, when a non-incumbent who spent $500,000 or more had an even chance of victory (Center for Responsive Politics, 2010).

While the convergence of politics and money is not always pretty, ignoring the importance of financial contributions to moving ones' legislative agenda forward is naïve at best and will ultimately undermine efforts to advance the positive aspects of the nursing profession's agenda. Nurses, like all other citizens, need to know at least the basics of what is happening in the political arena with respect to funding political campaigns. Because of the importance of political contributions, nurses should also provide financial support to those entities that are able to make strategic political contributions on their behalf. Unfortunately, when accounting for political contributions to federal candidates in 2010, contributions from nursing-focused groups ranked far below those of other healthcare-related interest groups. For example, according to information compiled by the Center for Responsive Politics, based on reports from the Federal Elections Commission as of April 25, 2011, the highest amount contributed to federal candidates in 2010 by a healthcare PAC (the National Association of Community Pharmacists) was $1,719,403. The American Nurses Association's contributions totaled only $582,911 during that same time frame (Center for Responsive Politics, 2011). It should therefore come as no surprise that organized nursing interests are at a disadvantage when trying to gain the ear of legislative decision-makers. Were it not for other sources of power—numbers and the general trusted reputation of the nursing profession—trying to gain a seat at the policy table would be an elusive aspiration at best.

Despite the need to know, following the money can be a difficult task: however, thanks to technology, it is not an impossible undertaking. State/county governmental websites include the campaign finance reports filed by political parties and candidates on the local level, and the Center for Responsive Politics (http://www.opensecrets.org) is a good resource for federal election funds. The first step is simply to gain an understanding of the critical role money plays in the process. While it may seem to undermine the integrity of policymaking, ignoring this reality will ensure frustration and likely failure.

Along with the money component of this leg of the stool, special interest groups also affect election outcomes by endorsing candidates running for office. Candidates who want to demonstrate their appeal to the overall electorate prize these endorsements; this is particularly true for endorsements issued by nurse organizations such as the

American Nurses Association on the federal level and state constituent associations of ANA on the state level. This level of political activity occurs through the associations' **political action committees (PACs)**. Federal and state election laws contain many requirements and restrictions a PAC must follow. For example, in order to participate in federal candidate advocacy, a federal PAC must be established and reporting requirements and contribution levels set forth in federal law adhered to. Similarly, if an organization wishes to endorse candidates seeking state office, it must set up a state PAC and follow state election laws. Generally, a federal PAC endorses candidates seeking a federal office such as the presidency or a congressional office, while state PACs focus on candidates running for state-wide offices such as governor, attorney general, secretary of state, and state legislative bodies. An endorsement may include monetary support for the campaign, or simply a publicized communication of support. According to Gallup's annual Honesty and Ethics survey released in December 2010, nurses continued to be recognized as the most trusted profession by the general public (Gallup, 2010); therefore, an endorsement from a nursing organization has value that transcends money.

Typically, organizations issuing endorsements have a process for doing so that can be fairly complex and usually involves a screening component. Decisions are based on criteria that take into consideration the political climate, the political index (the ratio of Republicans to Democrats to Independents in the district), the voting record of incumbents, and other intangible factors. While candidate endorsements can enhance an organization's perceived power, the decisions are not without risks both internally and externally. Externally, endorsing the "wrong" candidate—the loser—can have repercussions when trying to gain support for a legislative initiative from the elected official—the unendorsed winner—once the election is over. Internally, members of endorsing organizations who are unhappy about an endorsement decision may cancel their membership as a sign of protest, thus weakening the power in numbers that is especially important for nursing organizations.

Elections are inherently a partisan process where political party labels do matter. Nurses are not all Republicans or all Democrats, and the partisan nature of candidate endorsements is often distasteful and misunderstood. Endorsements, regardless of the political party of the candidate, are useful tools on several levels, however. First, exposing candidates to issues important to the nursing profession during the endorsement screening process is a way to educate potential lawmakers about these issues. Candidates are introduced to nurses who may be looked to as resources in the future when healthcare issues arise. Additionally, candidates who may not be particularly well versed about the complexities of the healthcare system receive information from a nursing perspective that they may not get elsewhere. Finally, an endorsement is not a directive to vote for a particular candidate, but serves as one more tool voters can use when making their own decisions. For nurses, an endorsement sends a signal that the candidate has participated in the screening process and appears to be someone nurses should seriously consider. Before reacting negatively to an endorsement decision made by a nursing organization, nurses should contact the organization to obtain more information as to why the decision was made. Voicing concerns to the decision-makers is productive, while cancelling membership serves only to undermine the profession's power base.

In addition to being aware of the inter-relational aspects of the legislative and political processes, it is also important to understand some of the labels attached to those who are players on the political stage. It is especially important when the labels mean different things to different people. For example, "One of the most incendiary words in today's political lexicon is *progressive*" (Moser, 2010, p. A-11). Members of the liberal wing of the Democratic Party use this term proudly, while conservatives use it as a term of reproach. For liberals, the word means "a set of policies (that) were attempts to address real problems that emerged in the development of an urban, industrial society. These policies have brought about immense tangible improvements in the lives of ordinary Americans" (Moser, p. A-11). Conservatives believe progressivism is an ideology that ignores the principles of limited government, separation of powers, and even unalienable individual rights that are the principles underlying the foundation of the United States. "The complexities of day-to-day operations of government make it necessary to take the operations out of the hands of the people themselves and entrust it instead to trained experts" (Moser, p. A-11) is a belief attributed to Liberals that Conservatives liken to fascism. According to Moser, "The problem is both sides are right, but neither seems willing to consider the other's definition" (p. A-11). Whether we can have a real national conversation or will simply continue to engage in the shouting match is unclear; however, some of the trends that are evolving make it more important than ever for all participants to speak the same language.

TRENDS AND TOOLS

Trends

I had endured plenty of rough politics in Texas. I had seen Dad and Bill Clinton derided by their opponents and the media. Abraham Lincoln was compared to a baboon. Even George Washington became so unpopular that political cartoons showed the hero of the American Revolution being marched to a guillotine. Yet the death spiral of decency during my time in office, exacerbated by the advent of twenty-four hour cable news and hyper-partisan political blogs, was deeply disappointing. The toxic atmosphere in American politics discourages good people from running for office. (Bush, 2010, p. 120)

Whether today's political climate is really nastier than in the past is debatable. "Perhaps the 19th-century political cartoons and stump speeches were uglier than anything seen today" ("In Search of Civility," 2010, p. A10), but today's technology enables these attacks to be more powerful because they spread "farther, faster, and linger longer" (p. A10). In addition to fueling what can be characterized as bully-like behavior, the power of technology gives more opportunity for citizen groups to develop, grow, and spread their message. The Tea Party movement is one such group, but others such as the "no labels" group are springing up. The trend of more citizen action is likely to continue, with its actual impact yet to be determined.

The Tea Party is characterized as a "conservative revolt" that is shaking up the Republican Party; however, the Democratic Party is not immune from the forces of unrest and frustration that gave rise to the movement. Generally, "Tea Partiers favor traditionally smaller government, unfettered financial markets, defanged regulation, and shrinking federal entitlements" (Scherer, 2010, p. 28). Whether Tea Partiers are the extremists they are portrayed to be, or whether their goals appeal to more main-stream Americans, remains to be seen. Thus far, there is no organizational structure for the Tea Party that parallels what is in place for the established Republican and Democratic parties; rather, it is a movement or loose aggregation of ideologues whose influence is fueled by evolving social media technology and a few dynamic individuals. The movement has generated enthusiasm, however. What also remains unclear is how much long-term impact it will have over the Republican Party and, ultimately, election outcomes. Candidates running for the U.S. Senate in seven states (Nevada, Colorado, Utah, Alaska, Kentucky, Delaware, and Florida) who were singled out for support by avowed Tea Partiers were victorious in the 2010 primary elections. They defeated Republican mainstream rivals, many of whom were handpicked by party leaders in Washington, D.C. Of the seven, four were successful in the general election.

Taking the stage after the 2010 election was a movement called the "no labels" group that purports to put aside traditional party labels in favor of a more centrist approach that espouses "doing what is best for America." "Political outliers—not quite Republican, not quite Democrat—are forming new alliances in a communal search for 'home'" (Parker, 2010, p. A13). The group thus far does not offer policy solutions to America's challenges; rather, it promotes civil behavior in public discourse. Its founders are high-ranking political operatives from both political parties, as well as candidates who lost an election because their positions were not liberal or conservative enough for the more extreme wings of their parties. Corporate backers include Andrew Tisch, co-chairman of Loews Corp.; Ron Shaich, founder of Panera Bread; and Dave Morin, ex-Facebook executive. The group kicked off its efforts in December 2010, so the extent of its impact remains unclear.

While the impact of technology and the fate of these emerging political groups are unclear, what is clear is the trend toward more dissatisfaction with the traditional two-party system that has controlled the political process. The ability of rogue groups fueled by the power of the Internet and other technology to form and send a widespread message will have an impact on election outcomes and campaign strategies in years ahead. The 2010 uprisings in Egypt and other Middle-Eastern countries are further evidence of the power that can be unleashed through electronic social networks. Nurses and nursing organizations should be aware of the potential of technology and use it to their advantage. Technology levels the power playing field and provides a cost-effective, far-reaching mechanism to leverage power that heretofore was available only to those with extensive resources at their disposal.

Tools

Although the political process itself may seem formidable, there are tools nurses can use to make participation feasible. Technology provides the information one needs to be an informed voter; however, it is often difficult to wade through the political rhetoric or to know who or what is the source for the information. Technology, although potentially useful, can be so overwhelming that its usefulness is lost in the clutter. Information from non-partisan sources can be especially useful in sorting out the kind of information being provided; the League of Women Voters and the Center for Responsive Politics are examples of two such sources. In addition, websites of professional nurse organizations often include governmental affairs links and background information that is available to members and, on a limited basis, to non-members.

Other tools:

- *EMILY's List:* Founded in 1985 by 25 women who understood the importance of money to the political process. EMILY—Early Money Is Like Yeast—raised $1 million by 1988 and over $10 million by 1992 in support of pro-choice Democratic women candidates. It issued its first presidential endorsement in 2007, supporting the candidacy of Hillary Clinton. While clearly targeted at Democratic women candidates, the organization has become a formidable political force whose interests often parallel those of nurses. EMILY's List is a network designed to provide its members with information about candidates and encourages them to write checks directly to the candidates. Its membership had grown to 600,000 by 2010 and, in addition to being a national PAC, it also provides training opportunities for potential women candidates running for state and local offices, prepares women to work in political campaigns, and has undertaken get-out-the-vote initiatives in targeted states. EMILY's List is credited with helping to elect 80 House members, 15 senators, and 9 governors.
- *WISH List (Women in the Senate and House):* Formed in 1992 to support pro-choice Republican women, it has contributed $3.5 million to its candidates since its inception, while also offering candidates advice and training opportunities.
- *The Susan B. Anthony List:* Formed in 1992 to support pro-life candidates and advance the pro-life agenda.

Federal and state government websites can be ready sources of information about the status of legislative initiatives, the individuals serving in elective offices, and the legislative process in general. These sites have links to all three branches of government (executive, legislative, and judicial) and can provide historical perspectives about past legislative sessions, as well as information on current ones. Federal legislative information is available through the Library of Congress at http://thomas.gov. You may also sign up for email alerts by contacting the offices of committee chairs and asking to be placed on their email lists.

When trying to decide which candidates to support in a particular election, candidates' nights can be especially useful, particularly those sponsored by nursing or healthcare-related organizations where the focus is often on healthcare issues. Audience members have a chance to see each candidate respond to questions and often can have an opportunity to talk to them one-on-one. While the candidates' answers to difficult questions may not be as responsive as one might wish, it could be instructive to see them in action.

What other tools can a nurse use to influence decisions around issues of importance, both professionally and more generally?

- First and foremost, vote. Voting records are readily available and people can easily check to see whether someone regularly exercises his/her right to vote. Being able to say "I am a voter in your district" with authority can make a difference in how the rest of the message is received.
- Be an informed voter. Do not rely on media messages; check out websites, attend candidates' nights, watch debates, and contact candidates directly through their campaigns to learn more about their philosophy and priorities.
- Volunteer to help during a campaign if a candidate seems especially knowledgeable/supportive of the nursing profession's issues. This can be as simple as addressing postcards or putting up a campaign sign to making phone calls or going door-to-door. Candidates remember those who help them, and doing so also provides an opportunity to get to know the candidate's staff and family members, many of whom are likely to have a strong influence over candidate perceptions and positions once the election ends.
- Contribute to a campaign and let the candidate know that the contribution comes from a nurse. Offer to hold a fundraiser or house party for the candidate. This level of assistence is very much appreciated by the candidate and can help gain access once the election is over.
- Letters to the editor provide an opportunity to express an opinion about a candidate or issue to a ready audience. Elected officials and candidates regularly monitor these communications, as do other readers.
- Write letters, call, or send email messages to elected officials to let them know how you feel about a particular issue. These messages, especially if not part of a mass mail/call initiative, can be very influential.

- Take advantage of resources provided by nursing organizations to keep informed about what is happening in a timely manner.
- Join a professional nurse organization and volunteer to be part of its political action arm. Let the organization know of your particular concerns and offer to testify should a legislative initiative arise that is within your areas of concern or expertise.
- Consider becoming part of organized political efforts in your county or voting district, such as county political parties or other efforts that will inevitably spring up through social media opportunities.
- Volunteer for committees (e.g. school districts, city council) doing foundational work that could become the basis for local policies.
- Join organizations such as the League of Women Voters to forge connections and gain a broader awareness of the political dynamics affecting decision-making.
- Run for office, locally, statewide, or nationally.

CONCLUSION

Then-State Representative Kevin DeWine (R-Fairborn), speaking at a Nurses' Day event at the Statehouse in Ohio, noted that the job of nurses and others is to make his life miserable. He then went on to rhetorically ask who wouldn't want a job that essentially offers a 2-year minimum contract for basically part-time work, and where no one pays attention to how you are doing the job. He concluded, "That is what you do if you don't hold me accountable for the decisions I make on a regular basis, not just on Election Day" (DeWine, personal communication, March 2005).

Holding elected officials accountable for their decisions means one must pay attention to what is happening in Washington and at statehouses on a regular basis. While politics may not be pretty, it is an integral part of how things get done. The decisions made by elected officials affect nursing practice and nurses' professional lives each and every day. To ensure a positive future for the nursing profession, as well as a healthcare system that reflects nurses' perspectives, nurses are required to engage in the political side of their profession. It need not be time-consuming, but it must become a more common occurrence that all nurses accept as essential to their professional practice.

RUNNING FOR ELECTIVE OFFICE—ONE NURSE'S EXPERIENCE

In 2008, after over 25 years of working in the state legislative arena as a lobbyist for nursing's interests, I became a candidate for the state House of Representatives. I had worked as a nurse in the clinical arena for many years and, after earning my Juris Doctor (JD), had practiced law as a healthcare attorney. I frequently spoke with nurses and nursing students about the importance of getting involved in the political process and often was asked why I didn't run myself. Heretofore, I had always managed to dismiss that possibility as far-fetched. Now healthcare reform was a major issue, along with education reform and the economy, and I soon became convinced that my background would appeal to voters who wanted change. Before proceeding, I had to make certain my family was on board, my employer would be supportive, and that I could put together a solid campaign team. If all those elements fell into place, I determined I would enter the race.

By the late fall of 2007, I had negotiated a satisfactory arrangement with my employer and was assured by my family that they were on board as well. In addition, I found campaign managers who were excited to take on the Lanier campaign to put a nurse in the statehouse! Although the incumbent was not eligible for re-election due to term limits, the race was not going to be easy. I was running as a Democrat in a very Republican district, and I faced a challenge in the primary election, which meant the campaign needed to get busy fast for the early March vote.

A March election meant campaigning during the cruel winter months. Climbing over snowdrifts to get signatures on candidate petitions, hammering campaign signs into frozen ground, and going door-to-door to meet voters in temperatures that would put Alaska to shame became routine. Was it fun? Not necessarily. But it was part of the job I signed on for when I said I wanted to be the candidate, so I did it almost without giving it a second thought.

In addition to the physical side, I also had to raise money to buy the signs, establish a credible web presence, and print the campaign literature being distributed on my behalf. That meant making phone calls and sending what I called my "begging letter" to everyone I could think of who might support the effort financially. There was no how-to book that really addressed all the aspects of campaigning, so I was learning on the job each day, every day.

Nurses were my best supporters and no one worked harder on our weekend "Nurses Make House Calls" initiatives. On the rainy, frigid-cold Election Day, nurses stood outside polling places with "Lanier" signs as one last reminder of who to look for on the ballot. That night, as the election results came trickling in, we soon learned that we had been successful, so there were a few moments of celebration with friends, family, and supporters. What a fun night! Winning made it all worthwhile. The next day, however, the campaign for the general election started its 8-month marathon.

This time, the snow had turned to warm/hot days with more time for meeting voters and raising those elusive funds. By the time the November election day arrived, I had knocked on over 10,000 doors personally, and the total neared 16,000 when the efforts of volunteers were included. We had participated in numerous local parades and attended candidates' nights, festivals, and fundraisers. Many special interest groups had issued valued endorsements of my candidacy, while others disappointingly endorsed my opponent. I had answered countless questionnaires about my position on every issue imaginable. We had designed a series of direct mail pieces and other materials to give voters a reason to vote for me. I survived some hurtful negative encounters with people who were convinced that my party affiliation meant I was un-American, and I learned to ignore cruel blog comments that were focused on the superficial, rather than genuine issues. I shared a stage with presidential candidate Barack Obama and was introduced by then-Senator Hillary Clinton at a local rally. I attended a VIP briefing with a United States senator and was treated to some remarkably frank discussions about how to address some of the serious problems affecting the state and the nation.

Throughout the process, I learned how many people were struggling with the challenges posed by job losses and foreclosures. I talked with people who could not get the health care they needed because they had lost or never had adequate health insurance coverage. I watched as volunteers set up a health clinic designed to serve economically disadvantaged people, many of whom were working in minimum wage jobs. I visited local farms, preschools, and a school for children with autism.

Despite all the efforts by so many, I did not win the seat in the House I worked so hard to attain. [Editor's note: Ms. Lanier won nearly 40% of the total vote, a remarkable feat as a Democrat in a highly Republican district. She is to be celebrated for this effort.] Winning is lots more fun than losing, so the November election night party was subdued at best. In the end, all agreed that we ran a good campaign and had no regrets or what ifs to carry around. Although the loss was incredibly disappointing, I have no second thoughts about taking the chance. I have a whole new understanding of and appreciation for the political process and politics in general. I met people I would never have met otherwise, and my life is richer for having done it. My family, particularly my grandchildren, got to experience a political campaign first hand. They know what it feels like to distribute candy during a parade and to do a "lit drop" through many neighborhoods.

So what is it like to be a candidate for an elective position that was not featured in the local media, one that was more people-focused than media driven?

- First and foremost, I found it to be one of the loneliest experiences of my life. Although I was constantly around people, I was really always on my own. Knocking on doors and never knowing what might be on the other side was disconcerting, but my nursing experience prepared me well to deal with whatever arose. I probably had more information about people's health status than the local health department!
- It was a very humbling experience with a huge learning curve. I learned how much I didn't know about the many issues facing people each day. I came to appreciate the unrealistic expectations we have for our elected officials. We elect people to state and federal legislatures expecting them to find solutions to all of the varied problems that challenge our cities, states, businesses, schools, industries, environment, and economy, and then do not give them the tools or time they need to be successful.

- I realized once I received my first campaign contribution that it was no longer about my own personal ambitions, but it was bigger than that. I now owed something to others; my best effort was put forth to ensure their trust in me was not misplaced. When I got tired or discouraged, I thought about the $5 contributions I received from retired nurses who wanted to help me in some way, and that kept me moving ahead. I also learned, sadly, how those big contributions really do have an impact. Because a campaign, even so-called down ticket races, are expensive and few people (especially a nonincumbent) can raise the dollars needed or expected to be a credible candidate, when someone or some group hands you a check with multiple zeros in the amount, it has an impact. That's a fact, like it or not.
- You cannot do it alone. A good team is essential—campaign manager, treasurer, volunteer coordinator, media/public relations/web specialist, and a constituency willing to work for you. Being a candidate is a full-time job. It was a year out of my life in which I had to be on my best behavior at all times because you never know who may be watching. My family members were also affected and had to be careful of what they said and did.
- Hard work alone will not result in a victory. Timing and location (district demographics—the political index) are critical factors as well. No candidate should run unopposed, however, so candidates should be encouraged to come forward. Voters should always have a genuine choice on Election Day. Sadly, the rigors of campaigning, including the personal scrutiny, discourage rather than encourage broad participation.
- People actually thanked me for running, which really surprised me.

Government is only as good as the people who hold elective office. Cynicism and a lack of participation will eventually doom our form of government. Partisanship needs to take a backseat to collaboration in order to solve the very serious problems facing all of us. Nurses can be candidates or part of a campaign team or simply a volunteer, but regardless of what they do, they should do something!

DISCUSSION POINTS AND ACTIVITIES

- Watch the HBO movie *Iron Jawed Angels*. What political considerations were at play in efforts to win voting rights for women? Have women today become complacent with respect to the importance of voting? Is the fight waged by suffragettes similar to the one nurses have waged to gain recognition of advanced practice? Describe. How does complacency imperil future professional advances for nursing?
- There are many metaphors for the future role of advanced practice nurses in the healthcare system. Select one of the metaphors below and describe the political considerations that come into play with respect to the selected metaphor.

1. The future role of advanced practice nurses is like a great roller coaster on a moonless night. It exists, twisting ahead of us in the dark, but we can only see the track that is just ahead. We are locked in our seats, and nothing we may know or do will change the course that is laid out for us; in other words, the future role is outside of our control.

2. The future role of advanced practice nurses is a huge game of dice. It is entirely random and subject only to chance. Since everything is chance, all we can do is play the game, pray to the gods of fortune, and enjoy what luck comes our way; in other words, the future is totally random and we do not know how or if our actions make a difference.

3. The future role of advanced practice nurses is like a great ship on the ocean. We can travel freely upon it and there are many possible routes and destinations. There will always be some outside forces, such as currents, storms, and reefs, to be dealt with, but we still have the choice to sail our ship where we want it to go; in other words, we can choose whatever future we want if we are willing to work with a purpose and within the knowledge and constraints of outside forces.

4. The future of advanced practice nurses is a blank sheet of paper. It is there for us to fill in with our actions and decisions in the present. If we choose the future we want and spend time within our professional lives trying to make it happen, it will probably materialize. If we leave it to the powers that be to decide upon and plan the future, we will have a very different kind of future—one dominated by traditional powerful forces. In other words, we have control over our future if we choose to act upon it.

Source: Adapted from Facing the Future, 2006.

For a full suite of assignments and additional learning activities, use the access code located in the front of your book to visit this exclusive website: http://go.jblearning.com/milstead. If you do not have an access code, you can obtain one at the site.

REFERENCES

American Association of Colleges of Nursing. (2011). Enhancing diversity in the nursing workforce. Retrieved from http://www.aacn.nche.edu/media/factsheets/diversity.htm

American Nurses Association. (2010). *Code of ethics for nurses.* Washington, DC: Author.

American Nurses Association. (2010). *Nursing's social policy statement.* Washington, DC: Author.

Brill, S. (2010, July 12). On sale: Your government. *Time, 176*(2), 28–33.

Bush, G. W. (2010). *Decision points.* New York, NY: Crown Publishers.

Center for Responsive Politics. (2010). The dollars and cents of incumbency. Retrieved from http://www. opensecrets.org/bigpicture/cost.php

Center for Responsive Politics. (2011). Health professionals. Retrieved from http://www.opensecrets.org/ pacs/industry.php:txt=H01&cycle=2010

Citizens United v. Federal Elections Commission (2010). 130 S. Ct. 876.

Crowley, M. (2010, September 27). The new GOP money stampede. *Time, 176*(13), 30–35.

deVries, C. M., & Vanderbilt, M. (1992). *The grassroots lobbying handbook.* Washington, DC: American Nurses Association.

Facing the Future. (2006). Lesson 38: Metaphors for the future. Retrieved from http://www.facingthefuture. org/Curriculum/DownloadFreeCurriculum/tabid/114/Default.aspx

Gallup. (2010). Nurses top honesty and ethics list for 11th year. Retrieved from http://www.gallup.com/ poll/145043/nurses-top-honesty-ethics-list-11-year.aspx

In search of civility [editorial]. (2010, December 21). *Columbus Dispatch*, p. A10.

Institute of Medicine. (2010). *Future of nursing report.* Washington, DC: The National Academies Press.

Lanier, J. (1985). *Power, politics, and the nurse.* In L. DeYoung (Ed.), *Dynamics of Nursing* (5th ed., pp. 166–178). St. Louis, MO: C.V. Mosby Company.

Moser, J. (2010, November 9). "Progressive" means different things to different people. *Columbus Dispatch*, p. A11.

O'Bryne, P., & Holmes, D. (2009). The politics of nursing care. *Policy, Politics, and Nursing Practice, 10*(2), 153–157.

Parker, K. (2010, November 30). Moderates are looking for a new home. *Washington Post/Columbus Dispatch*, A13.

Patterson, K. (2011). Top bill: How to influence lawmakers. *Nursing Spectrum/Nurse Week.* Retrieved from http://news.nurse.com/article/20110124/national01/101240027/-1/frontpage

Scherer, M. (2010, September 27). It's tea time. *Time, 176*(13), 26–29.

Conclusion: A Policy Toolkit for Healthcare Providers and Activists

Roby Robertson
and
Donna Middaugh

OVERVIEW

What is the role of the healthcare professional in the political process? Given the range of issues addressed in this book, where does the political process begin and end? This healthcare policy book is centered on the notion that all healthcare providers require a fundamental understanding of the healthcare system that is not limited to the knowledge required to practice their discipline. No longer can healthcare professionals be prepared solely for clinical practice, but they must ready themselves to deal with the economic, political, and policy dimensions of health care because the services they provide are the outcome of these dynamics.

OBJECTIVES

- To define the role of the healthcare professional in policy advocacy and politics
- To describe processes for becoming a policy advocate within one's own organization and beyond
- To recognize the difference between expertise and internal and external advocacy in relation to stakeholders
- To apply the concepts of health policy to case study vignettes
- To develop one's own toolkit for becoming a health policy advocate

KEY TERMS

- ❑ Advocacy
- ❑ Constituent
- ❑ Expertise
- ❑ External stakeholder

(continues)

❑ Internal stakeholder   ❑ Power
❑ Politics   ❑ Stakeholder

This book offers an interdisciplinary approach to understanding healthcare practice and policy. Professional nurses and other allied health practitioners must have a seat at the policy table, but they must also understand the perspectives of their colleagues; therefore, we have used contributors from outside of nursing, including allied health professionals, activists, politicians, economists, and policy analysts who understand the forces of health care in America, to frame this textbook. The rationale behind an interdisciplinary approach is that no one person has the right solution to the challenges confronting health care in America. These challenges include high costs, limited access, medical errors, variable quality, administrative inefficiencies, and a lack of coordination.

It is not surprising that the healthcare system is under serious stress and that a host of actors both within and beyond the system have myriad solutions to the problem. This chapter suggests that politics is both necessary and critical to making changes, whether we are discussing system level reforms (e.g., national health insurance reform) or a local hospital improving health data access (e.g., electronic medical records). This textbook offers current and future healthcare practitioners who are committed to reducing health disparities and achieving healthcare equality insight into how clinical practice is derived from regulations and laws that are based on public policy and politics.

This book provides an overview of the essential elements that drive health policy in the United States. Within these pages, the reader has been given the following:

- A compelling rationale for engaging in health policy issues
- A thorough review of the healthcare delivery labor force

- An appreciation of the role of markets and government in the system of healthcare finance
- A description of how power, markets, and government affect healthcare organizations and the delivery of care
- Insight into key drivers of the organization of healthcare services, namely technology, quality, and research

This final chapter provides healthcare practitioners a toolkit or a working model of how to "do" policy advocacy within and beyond our organizational lines. This chapter answers these questions: "What is the health professional's role in policy advocacy and politics?" "What are the major distinctions in affecting policy through the two primary areas addressed in this book?" This chapter examines two broad components of policy change—the influence and power of stakeholders/constituencies and the power of expertise. These arenas overlap; of course, here we examine them separately to portray their specific roles more accurately.

What then is the healthcare practitioner's role in the political process? Where does that process take place? Many traditional views define the political process as external only, primarily defined at the policy-making levels of government or boards and commissions; therefore, the argument follows that professionals below senior-level decision makers are primarily reactive; that is, they respond to proposals from up the line and/or must calculate how to implement the changes that others have imposed on them.

In public administration, this has traditionally been defined as a politics/administration dichotomy; that is, political decisions are made by higher ups, and the administrator finds a way to carry out those decisions. In public administration and related policy fields, however, that dichotomy is no more because in actual decision-making and in the practicalities of day-to-day management, interactions at all levels of the organization are necessary to the practice of management/policy formulation and implementation. The administrators are trying to influence policy outcomes like those in the policy arena. And practitioners should do the same.

There is also another reason why practitioners must develop a political/policy toolkit. Politics and policy making are not a function only of the external environment of the organization. In fact, the most sophisticated and nuanced elements of such a policy/political role can be found also in the *internal environment* of the organization. Again, practitioners can play a role influencing these outcomes.

Imagine the following scenario. Your senior executive pulls you aside one day and says, "Do you know that proposal you've wanted to push forward about how we reallocate the staff here in the organization? Well, why don't you put together the budget, a time line, and what we need to do to move this forward in the next budget cycle?" You have been anxious to do so for some time, and you stay in the office every evening putting together the proposal (with fancy pie charts, a time line, personnel requirements, etc.), and you turn it in to your executive.

A week goes by and then two and then three. You are getting anxious; to do some of the time line issues you would need to get rolling soon, but you've heard nothing. You mention it to the executive and she nods, looks solemn, and asks you back into the office. She sits on the edge of the desk (not behind the desk, not a good sign) and pulls out your proposal. You can see it has been marked up with lots of red marks throughout. The executive shakes her head and says, "Well it really is a great idea; it really is the way

to go in the future, but I ran it up the line, and well, you know, 'politics got in the way.' It's just not going to fly!" She hands back your proposal. You return to your office and open the file cabinet of other projects that didn't get off the ground, and you think, politics!

Well? Why didn't it fly? What could have happened? Senior managers did not like the proposal? It competed with other proposed changes that could "fly." What kept yours from flying? Perhaps it was because you had not accounted for the politics of your own organization. Politics exist at the organizational level, not just at the policy-making level, and you sat back and allowed others to make the decision. Thus, our approach in this chapter is to suggest that the politics of the environment are both external and internal.

We suggest that the key to gaining more effective use of the policy environment, both inside and outside the organization, is to understand more effectively the *power* that one has to effect change. Unlike many analyses of power that are often based on the individual, our approach is to examine the organizational power that exists for the practitioner/advocate. We examine that power through two broad arenas—the power of stakeholder relationships and the power of expertise.

Figure 1 is a simple heuristic about power. This simple pyramid has been widely used in political science and policy fields for years. Power can be seen in the levels of the pyramid, with the narrowest (and thus the weakest type of power) at the top of the pyramid and becoming broader with more effective types of power moving down the pyramid. *Force* we all understand. The power to make others do things by forcing them to do so is obvious, from the actual use of force (including weapons) through the more common use of force in an organization which is the power of the organization to enforce rules, standards, and practices. *Influence* is more nuanced, but its role is also obvious—does the organization have the capacity to convince others that they should support or acquiesce to the organization's decision? There are many reasons why an organization may be able to influence a decision. Possibly the organization has shown in the past the capacity to be successful; maybe it is because the organization has demonstrated knowledge or connections to accomplish the tasks required. Nevertheless, the organization must convince others that its decisions are good. Finally, the broadest and most critical part of the power pyramid is *authority*. At the core of a lot of political theory about the state is authority—the acceptance of the organization to decide and the acceptance by others of its decisions without serious question. Expertise is one form of authority. We tend to accept the recommendations of those who are expert in a field.

One example of how all three elements of the power triangle work is driving your car late at night and stopping at a red light with nobody around. There you sit because a light bulb with a red cover over it is "on"! Now, that is power! Do you recognize why you stopped? Did you have to be convinced (well, maybe you think for a second that lights regulate traffic, but it is the middle of the night and there are no cars

Figure 1 Power pyramid.

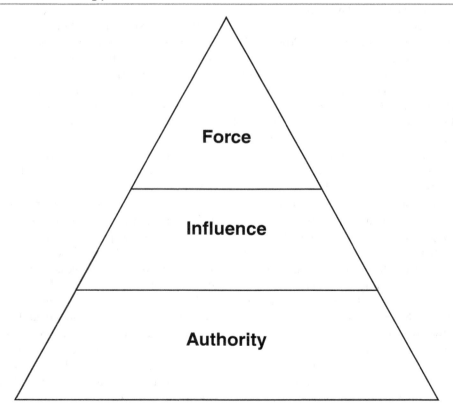

around!)? Do you run the light? Not right away because you first look around to see whether there is a police car around! Now, all three elements are in play, and you stopped at the light in the first place because? It turned red, and you stop at red lights!

Thus, how do we understand our power in organizations? Obviously, there are multiple elements in this—from the regulatory environment, the level of federalism, the growth of the state, and so forth. Here we summarize around two broad elements that undergird the organization's power: stakeholders and expertise. We are going to distinguish between internal and external power (power within the organization and beyond) (see Figure 2).

Stakeholder Power

For many in the healthcare arena, stakeholder power seems the most obvious political tool: A simple "who do you know, who is on our side" model of developing policy change is obvious. Too often, however, our approach is to simply add up the influentials on "our side" and on the "other side." The stakeholder list becomes a list of names, rather than a list of the nature of power relationships. Well, if it is just numbers, then

Figure 2 Focus and locus of organizational power.

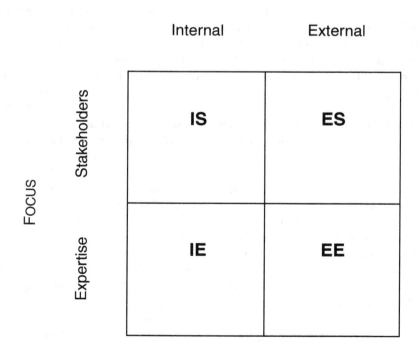

any policy supported by a greater number of individuals or organizations should prevail. Under those conditions, we would suggest that a national health system that is effective for the poor would be the easiest to pass, but somehow one knows that organizations representing low-income groups have less influence than those representing higher income groups. Right? So, it cannot be just numbers!

Thus, stakeholder analysis is tied to the network of stakeholders and which sets of stakeholders are closer to your organization and which are more distant. This close/distant issue is often defined in terms of natural and face-to-face relationships: ideally, what groups deal with your agency and/or policy arena on a routine and constant basis and what groups deal with your organization on a more limited basis. Thus, the classic stakeholder map often has concentric circles of groups and organizations closer and further away from the organization based on the level of interdependence and organizational closeness (Fottler et al., 1989). If you represent a Veterans' hospital, for example, members of veterans' organizations, such as the American Legion or Veterans of Foreign Wars, are more central to your organization, but if you are working from a children's hospital, that organizational tie is irrelevant. Thus, understanding how central other stakeholders are to the organization may be the first part of a stakeholder analysis (Figure   3).

To understand stakeholder power for an organization, however, one must define it in terms of *organized* stakeholders. When working with various healthcare organizations, we often hear stakeholders described in individual terms (e.g., patients or customers), but the key is to recognize the importance of having stakeholders who are organized and have well-defined structures. For example, "veterans" is a vague definition for a set of stakeholders, but American Legion or

Veterans of Foreign Wars are two critical organized groups who represent veterans.

What if there is no organized set of stakeholders? The first question might be this: Why is that true? It might be that the stakeholders in the external environment that your organization deals with are too amorphous to be defined. In James Q. Wilson's (1989) terminology, you may represent a majoritarian organization that has no discernible set of constituents or stakeholders other than the public. If that is the case, stakeholder power will be more limited for your organization.

However, we have found that many organizations have developed stakeholder groups over time (often for nonpolitical reasons), which generates some level of influence. One of our favorite examples comes from outside the healthcare arena—police departments. If one thinks about natural constituents or stakeholders, then police departments' most obvious stakeholders are those who commit crimes—not sure how to build a stakeholder group there! Over time, police departments have developed a host of support organizations, including neighborhood watch groups. The reason for their creation is not to influence political decisions about police departments, but strong neighborhood watch groups (organized across a city) can become a critical secondary stakeholder group for a police department. Who organized those neighborhood watches? Generally, police departments took the lead in doing so and the neighborhood watch groups typically support what is being proposed by the police department.

The example of a children's hospital is appropriate here. One might argue that on a day-to-day basis, the constituents of such a hospital are the patients. They are children, but maybe we would include the parents. What about parent groups? Well, generally, they have limited interest in being stakeholders of the hospital; in

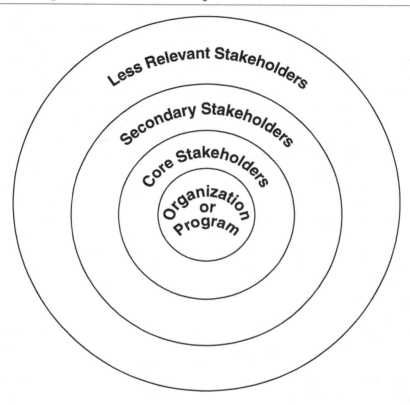

fact, they want to get their children well and leave the hospital. What about children suffering from a chronic illness or a long-term disease such as cancer? Most such hospitals have developed parent and children groups to get together from time to time to support each other (and to provide additional information to the hospital and to other patients and their families about coping with the illness). If the hospital's outreach department has helped organize the group so that it sets officers and meeting dates, then the group is now organized! Is it the same as a veterans' organization? Clearly not, but it would be wise to include such a group in any efforts to ad-

vocate for policy changes (inside and beyond the hospital).

Expertise

What is expert power in an organization? Some would define it in terms of knowledge acquisition and professionalism. Thus, an expert organization would have a high proportion of highly educated professionals, defined by advanced education, licensure, professional norms and ethical standards, and a lifetime of continuing education. The healthcare arena has a clear advantage here. The various professions within any existing healthcare arena are often complex, and they have specialized education, training, and licensure at virtually every level of professional delivery of services. Such professionalized organizations often begin with a noticeable advantage over other organizations in which there is little or no professionalized work force.

Thus, any definition of organizational expertise must begin with the nature of the expertise of the organization and whether it is well developed and professionalized and of the highest educational standards; however, one must be careful about defining this power simply as a set of acquired educational/professional standards. In the end, it is a bit like our traffic light—all of the diplomas, certificates, and licensure do not necessarily mean that the expertise is perceived as powerful. Similar to the number of stakeholders not being as important as the proximity of stakeholders to the decision makers, not all experts carry equal weight when it comes to organizational decisions.

What is the key to this expertise? It is the perception of others that the expertise is legitimate. Many healthcare professionals blunder here because they believe that achievement of a variety of graduate/professional degrees leads automatically to support of their expertise. To put it in simple terms, many occupations (especially in the healthcare arena) are licensed, certified, and with advanced education but thus do not have equal expertise power. Why? Maybe because the public or the broader political/policy environment does not differentiate the various specializations, or the expertise of the profession is recognized strongly only by the profession itself. The best example today is the widespread public agreement about the need for more nurses. How does that translate generally? Does the public differentiate well between LPN, RN, diploma, AD, BSN, MSN, NP, CRNA, CNS, or advanced practice nurses? No! Why not? Does

the public see the difference between a general practitioner in medicine and a specialist in oncology? Yes! What is the difference here? We would suggest that the public has become convinced (generally through well-defined efforts by the medical establishment) that there are differences in behavior in the various medical specializations and that some of them have more expertise power because the public perceives them as more expert. Why is that not as true in the field of nursing? We suggest that part of the explanation is that the nursing profession has been reluctant to emphasize publically the differences between the various areas of nursing professionalism. We would suggest that this limits the political capacity of the various specializations to garner separate political support.

Thus, building expertise power in an organizational setting must also include addressing some important issues, not the least of which is the belief that the expertise of the particular set of professionals is desired by others in the policy environment. Internally, in a hospital, for example, when policy is being made about how practices are implemented, changed, evolved, or reorganized, is the profession you represent at the table in the discussion? If not, why not?

Thus, as we develop the toolkit for expert power, we must ask a critical question: "Who believes this expertise is valued and should be represented in the decision making process (both within and beyond the organization)?"

Toolkit Case Studies

The case studies included in this toolkit chapter are designed to aid the reader in understanding the politics of organizational power. They are divided based on four categories: external stakeholder, internal stakeholder, external expertise, and internal expertise. Each of these real-life case studies illustrates how health professionals have applied the tools as highlighted within this chapter. The case study authors have included references for the reader's use, when applicable. To guide your comprehension and application of the toolkit, the authors have included several thought provoking questions at the end of each case study. Readers are encouraged to critically analyze the political methods and power used in each case study, exploring the stakeholders and type of expertise involved. The questions following each case study are helpful for group discussion, as well as individual analysis. This chapter concludes with one additional case study that has not had any sort of political result to date, and readers are asked to analyze that case in terms of how one might build the necessary political stakeholder and expert power.

External Expert Power

The first two cases presented here are doubtless well known to readers, but what may not be well known is the history of the development of policy in these areas. As you examine these two case studies, remember that their purpose is to show the role of expertise in affecting policy.

CASE STUDY

Margaret Sanger as Nurse and Public Health Advocate

Ellen Chesler

"No Gods, No Masters," the rallying cry of the Industrial Workers of the World, was her personal and political manifesto. Emma Goldman and Bill Haywood, Mabel Dodge, and John Reed were among her earliest mentors and comrades. Allied with labor organizers and bohemians, Margaret Sanger first emerged on the American scene in those halcyon days at the turn of the 20th century when the country seemed wide open with possibility, before world war, revolution, and repression provided a more sober reality.

She organized pickets and protests and pageants in the hope of achieving wholesale economic and social justice. What began as a callow faith in revolution quickly gave way to a more concrete agenda for reform. Working as a visiting nurse on New York's Lower East Side, she watched a young patient die tragically from the complications of a then-all-too-common illegal abortion and vowed to abandon palliative work and devote herself instead to single-minded pursuit of reproductive autonomy for women.

Sanger proudly claimed personal freedom for women. She also insisted that the price women pay for equality should not be the sacrifice of personal fulfillment. Following in the footsteps of a generation of suffragists and social welfare activists who had forgone marriage in order to gain professional stature and public influence, she became the standard bearer of a less ascetic breed, intent on balancing work and family obligations.

The hardest challenge in writing this history for modern audiences, for whom these claims have become routine, is to explain how absolutely destabilizing they seemed in Sanger's time. Even with so much lingering animus toward women's rights today, it is hard to remember that reproduction was once considered a woman's principal purpose, and motherhood, her primary role—that women were assumed to have no need for identities or rights independent of those they enjoyed by virtue of their relationships to men—and that this principle was central to the long-enduring opposition they have faced in seeking rights to work, to inheritance and property, to suffrage, and most especially to control of their own bodies.

Sanger needed broader arguments. By practicing birth control, women would not just serve themselves, she countered. They would also lower birthrates, alter the balance of supply and demand for labor, alleviate poverty, and thereby achieve the aspirations of workers without the social upheaval of class warfare. Not the dictates of Karl Marx, but the refusal of women to bear children indiscriminately would alter the course of history, a proposition ever resonant today as state socialism becomes an artifact of history, while family planning, although still contested, endures with palpable consequences worldwide.

In 1917, Sanger went to jail for distributing contraceptive pessaries to immigrant women from a makeshift clinic in a tenement storefront in the Brownsville section of Brooklyn. Classic elements of modernization, including urbanization, industrialization, and secularization, were already driving down the nation's birthrate as a result of private contraceptive arrangements and a healthy underground trade in condoms, douches, and various contraptions. Sanger's contribution was to demand services for the poor that were available to the middle class. Her heresy, if you will, was in bringing the issue of sexual and reproductive freedom out in the open and claiming it as a woman's right. She staged her arrest deliberately to challenge New York's already anachronistic obscenity laws—the legacy of the notorious Anthony Comstock, whose evangelical fervor had captured Victorian politics, in a manner eerily reminiscent of our time—and led to the adoption by the federal government and the states of broad criminal sanctions on sexual speech and commerce, including all materials related to contraception and abortion. Zealous protector of traditional values and "savior" of vulnerable single women, Comstock had himself authorized as a special agent of the U.S. Post Office, with the power to undertake searches and make arrests. He died of pneumonia in 1915, after repeated confrontations with Sanger and her supporters that generated widespread publicity and sympathy for her cause, transforming it from a radical gesture to a cause célèbre.

Direct action tactics served Sanger well, but legal appeal of her clinic conviction also established a medical exception to New York's Comstock Law. Doctors—although not nurses, as she originally intended—were granted the right to prescribe contraception for health purposes, and under that constraint, she built the modern family planning movement with independent, free-standing facilities as the model for distribution of services, a development that occurred largely in spite of leaders of the medical profession, who remained shy of the subject for many years and did not formally endorse birth control until 1937, well after its scientific and social efficacy was demonstrated.

By then, Sanger and Hannah Stone, the medical director of her New York clinic, had also achieved another legal breakthrough. They prevailed in a 1936 federal appellate court decision in New York that licensed physicians to import contraceptive materials and use the federal mails for their transport. The ruling effectively realized years of failed efforts to achieve legislative reform in Congress, although it did formally override prohibitions that remained in several states until the historic ruling in *Griswold* with its claim of a constitutional doctrine of privacy, later extended so controversially to abortion in *Roe v. Wade*.

Sanger had long since jettisoned political ideology for a more reasoned confidence in the ability of education and science to shape human conduct and in the possibility of reform through bold public health initiatives. Her most prominent mentor through this passage was H.G. Wells, the renowned British man of letters and influence, who foresaw the development of states that would mix free markets with centralized planning for social welfare. Both became tribunes for the rational, scientific control of the world's population and its resources, with Wells giving Sanger international credibility and enhancing her stature.

With hard work and determination, she was able to mobilize men of influence in business, labor, academia, and the emerging professions. No less critical to her success was her decision to invest in the collective potential of women, many of whom had been oriented to activism by the suffrage movement and were eager for a new cause after finally winning the vote in 1920. She also lobbied the churches, convincing the clerical establishments of the progressive Protestant and Jewish denominations of the virtue of lifting sexuality and reproduction from the shroud of myth and mystery to which traditional faiths had long consigned them. She even won a concession from the hierarchy of the American Catholic Church, which overruled the Vatican and endorsed natural family planning, or the so-called rhythm method, as a way of countering the secular birth control movement and reasserting religious authority over values and behavior.

With an uncanny feel for the power of well-communicated ideas in a democracy, Sanger moved beyond women's rights to put forth powerful public health and social welfare claims for birth control. She proved herself a savvy public relations strategist and an adept grass-roots organizer. Through the 1920s and 1930s, she wrote best-selling books, published a widely read journal, crisscrossed the country, and circled the globe, giving lectures and holding conferences that attracted great interest and drove even more publicity. She built a thriving voluntary movement to conduct national and state-level legislative lobbying and advocacy work and to work in communities on the ground, sustaining affiliate organizations that organized and operated pioneering women's health clinics. Offering a range of medical and mental health services in reasonably sympathetic environments, many of these facilities became laboratories for her idealism.

Yet the birth control movement stalled during the long years of the Great Depression and World War II, stymied by the increasing cost and complexity of reaching those most in need and overwhelmed by the barrage of opposition it engendered. The issue remained mired in moral and religious controversy, even as its leadership determinedly embraced a centrist politics and a sanitized message. When hard times encouraged attention to collective needs over individual rights and when the New Deal legitimized public responsibility for economic and social welfare, Sanger cannily replaced the "birth control" moniker with the more socially resonant content of "family planning." Both were terms she invented and popularized after consulting allies and friends. These strategies of accommodation, however, did nothing to stop officials of the National Catholic Welfare Conference and other opponents from making the most scandalous accusations that birth control was killing babies, waging war on poor families, even causing the depression itself by slowing population growth and lowering consumer demand, a proposition that some economists of the day also endorsed.

Having enjoyed Eleanor Roosevelt's enthusiastic support and personal friendship in New York, Sanger went to Washington in the 1930s hoping that Congress would overturn the Comstock law and legalize contraceptive practice as a first step to her long-term goal of transferring responsibility and accountability for services from small, privately funded clinics to public health programs with appropriate resources and scale; however, she failed to anticipate that the success of the Roosevelt's would depend on a delicate balancing of the votes

of conservative urban Catholics in the north and rural, fundamentalist Protestants in the south. There would be no invitations to tea at the White House and no government support, at least until Franklin was safely ensconced in a third term.

What is more, the ever-fragile alliance Sanger built with the country's elites itself became a liability. Sanger resigned from the American Birth Control League she had founded, severing official ties with others in the movement who boldly advanced contraception as a means of slowing birthrates among the poor. Her own politics had long tended to the left, and she became an enthusiastic New Dealer. She offered family planning not as a panacea but as a piece of a broader package of health and social welfare policies that would also provide economic and social safety nets. She framed poverty as a matter of differential access to resources, including contraception, not as the immutable consequence of low inherent ability or bad character, a view held by many conservatives. She spoke out against immigration restrictions, held advanced views on race, and enjoyed enthusiastic support for her work from W.E.B. Dubois, from many others in the progressive black community, and eventually from Mrs. Roosevelt, whose commitments to civil rights were well known.

Like other well-intended social reformers of her day, Sanger also endorsed eugenics, the then ubiquitous and popular movement that addressed the manner in which biological factors affect human, health, intelligence, and opportunity. She took away from Darwinism the essentially optimistic lesson that man's common descent in the animal kingdom makes us all capable of improvement, if only we apply the right tools. Believing that ability and talent should replace birthright and social status as the standard of mobility in a democratic society, she endorsed intelligence testing, an enduring legacy of this era, and she did not repudiate the infamous Supreme Court decision of 1929 in *Buck v. Bell* that mandated compulsory sterilization on grounds of feeble-mindedness. She also supported the payment of bonuses to women who volunteered for sterilization because they wanted no more children.

These compromised views placed her squarely in the intellectual mainstream of her time and in the good company of many progressives who shared these beliefs. Still, her failure to consider the validity of standard assessments of aptitude or the fundamental rights questions inherent in these procedures has left her vulnerable in hindsight to attacks of insensitivity and bigotry. The family planning movement at home and abroad has long been burdened by the charges that it fostered prejudice, even as it delivered welcome services and relief from unwanted childbirth to women in need.

Embittered by these controversies and disenchanted with the country's increasing pronatalism after World War II, Sanger turned her attentions abroad. In 1952, she founded the International Planned Parenthood Federation, with headquarters in London, as an umbrella for the national family planning associations that remain today in almost every country in the world.

By the time of her death in 1966, the cause for which she defiantly broke the law had achieved international stature. Although still a magnet for controversy, she was widely eulogized as one of the great emancipators of her time. She lived to see the United States Supreme Court provide constitutional protection to the use of contraceptives in *Griswold v. Connecticut.* She watched Lyndon Johnson incorporate family planning into America's social welfare and foreign policy programs, fulfilling her singular vision of how to advance opportunity and prosperity, not to speak of human happiness, at home and abroad. A team of doctors and scientists she had long encouraged marketed the oral anovulant birth control pill, and a resurgent feminist movement gave new resonance to her original claim that women have a fundamental right to control their own bodies.

In the years since, however, further controversy has surrounded the practices of what developed as often alarmist global population control efforts that adopted rigid demographic targets and imposed harsh, unwelcome, and culturally insensitive technologies on women. Population policy makers and service providers have been fairly criticized for abusing rights by ignoring or downplaying the risks of providing costly technologies where health services are inadequate to cope with potential complications and where failure rates have been high, even though these products are medically benign when properly administered.

In 1994, the United Nations International Conference on Population and Development in Cairo created a framework for state responsibility to ensure programs allowing women to make free and informed decisions about family planning, but also obligating access to comprehensive, reproductive health services of high quality, including birth control. The benefit of effective family planning to the well-being of individuals, families, and communities was officially acknowledged, despite continued resistance from the Vatican and some conservative Islamic states. Population and development professionals, however, also committed to a doctrine that weds policies and practices to improvements in women's status—to education, economic opportunity, and basic civil rights for women subject to culturally sanctioned discrimination and violence—just as Margaret Sanger first envisioned.

Hundreds of millions of women and men around the world today freely practice some method of contraception, with increasing reliance again on condoms, in light of the epidemic spread of HIV-AIDS and other sexually transmitted infections. This represents a sixfold increase since rates of population growth peaked in the 1960s.

Still, half the world's population today—nearly 3 billion people—are under the age of 25 years. Problems associated with widespread poverty, food insecurity, and environmental degradation are widespread. There remains considerable unmet need for family planning and tragically insufficient funding for research on new methods and for new programming to meet ever-increasing demand. Funding for both population and development programs has slowed dramatically, as other needs compete for funds and as concern now spreads instead about an aging and shrinking population in many countries in the global north and south where birthrates have declined sharply. The cycles of history repeat themselves.

Case Study Questions

At what points did the science of birth control precede any change in policy/practice in this area? Why do you think that was the case? Why was the expertise of effective birth control not widely shared, and why did it take the medical establishment so long to endorse policy change in this area? Clearly, the women's movement was part of the opening of change in this area, but how did it contribute to the creation of knowledge? What happened to the policy of birth control after the American Medical Association supported it in the 1930s? Why did it take another 30 years for birth control to be widely available to women in America? Have there been changes in recent years in the broader environment that are analogous to the early adoption of birth control programs (e.g., RU 487 or the "morning after" pill)? Have these changes increased or limited access to birth control? Think through the acceptance of the expertise in this area and the ways in which it has contributed (or limited) the change in policy in this environment and the ways in which it has not been taken into account. Can you illustrate how expertise is still about perception, both within professional fields as well as in the broader public?

CASE STUDY

The Centers for Disease Control's 2006 Recommendations on Screening for HIV Infection

Kathleen M. Nokes

HIV is the virus that causes AIDS. Because this diagnosis is consistent with severe immune depression, a person can be infected with HIV for many years before AIDS develops (Centers for Disease Control [CDC], 2007). Except for newborns, all persons who test positive for the antibody to the HIV are diagnosed with HIV infection. Antibody testing is cheaper than direct viral testing for genetic evidence of HIV. HIV antibody testing first became available in 1985 and was primarily used to increase the safety of the blood supply; by 1987, the United States Public Health Service issued guidelines making counseling and testing a priority as a prevention strategy. Extensive guidelines structured the counseling session before persons agreed to consent to HIV testing, and it was emphasized that infected persons needed to avoid transmitting the virus and at-risk persons needed to adopt behaviors to decrease their risk. In 1993, the CDC recommended voluntary testing for hospitalized patients as well as outpatients in acute-care hospitals and emergency departments. Hospitals with high inci-

dence rates were encouraged to adopt a policy of offering voluntary HIV counseling and testing routinely to all patients aged 15 to 54 years (CDC, 2006). The CDC focused on screening pregnant women and did not turn their attention back to hospitalized patients again until 10 years later, in 2003. Over that period, HIV infection transitioned from a terminal to chronic illness because of the development of effective strategies to control the infection and immune damage caused by HIV.

HIV infection is a stigmatizing condition. In order to encourage persons to learn their HIV status, extensive confidentiality laws were enacted that required that persons *choose* when and if they will be screened for HIV infection. Written informed consent was mandated in some states, including New York State, so that persons would be aware that their blood was being tested for HIV infection. When persons learned that they were HIV positive, not only were they concerned about their physical health, but there were consequences impacting relationships, personal safety, and economics as well as mental health. Because HIV infection can persist for years before significant symptoms are manifested, many persons chose to avoid the stress of learning their HIV status and continued in their day-to-day activities. Because HIV is transmitted from one person to another, there is also a sense of betrayal and anger that an intimate interaction resulted in danger, reflecting a lack of caring.

By 2003, the CDC acknowledged that hospitalized patients were not being routinely offered voluntary screening and cited lack of reimbursement for HIV screening, inadequate time for healthcare providers to conduct risk assessments and adequate counseling, and lack of explicit information about HIV prevalence as reasons for the low screening rates. After extensive consultation with key stakeholders, the CDC issued the *Revised Recommendations for HIV Testing of Adults, Adolescents, and Pregnant Women in Health-care Settings* in 2006. This case study examines components of these recommendations from a policy perspective. This policy analysis focuses on the two sections of the recommendations related to screening for HIV infection and consent and pretest information for nonpregnant women. To quote from page 7 of the *Morbidity and Mortality Weekly Report* of September 22, 2006:

In all health-care settings, screening for HIV infection should be performed routinely for all patients aged 13-64 years. Healthcare providers should initiate screening unless prevalence of undiagnosed HIV infection in their patients has been documented to be less than 0.1%.

In 1993, the CDC recommended screening persons aged 15 to 54 years, compared with the 2006 recommendation of ages 13 to 64 years. The lower age limit of 13 reflects the pediatric classification of AIDS, in which it is believed that infection occurred perinatally from the HIV infected mother to the fetus and/or infant. The decision to establish any upper age limit for routine screening in healthcare facilities, however, seems arbitrary. Of course, although it can be clearly established by looking at the 2006 prevalence data that while the highest percentage (22%) of persons living with AIDS were aged 40 to 44 (CDC, 2008), the number of persons older than age 64 diagnosed with HIV/AIDS increased only from 570 to 618 between the years 2003 and 2006 (CDC, 2008, Table 1) or less than 1% of the cases diagnosed in those years.

Nevertheless, the underlying rationale of the CDC for the 2006 recommendation is that approximately one quarter of the persons infected with HIV are unaware of their infection and therefore are not accessing treatment or engaging in preventing the spread of HIV infection. With any arbitrary upper age limit for routine HIV screening in healthcare facilities, we will never know the number of older persons who are living with HIV/AIDS. An argument for creating an upper age limit might be to avoid the cost associated with widespread HIV screening in very low-incidence populations, but the second part of the screening recommendations addresses this by instituting routine screening only in prevalence areas of more than 1%. New York has the highest prevalence case rate for adults with HIV infection (not AIDS) in the United States (261.7 per 100,000) (CDC, 2008, p. 8), and most of those New York cases live in New York City.

New York City reports the age category of 60 years or older and 8% of all the persons living with HIV or AIDS in NYC as of December 31, 2006, were in that age category compared with 24.5% of persons aged 50 to 59 years. From the time of HIV infection to the development of AIDS, as many as 10 to 12 years can elapse. There is thus every possibility that the numbers of cases of older persons are underreported, especially in an area with an established epidemic and high prevalence; nevertheless, the policy makers in New York are mirroring CDC recommendations to provide routine screening for persons only up to age 64 years. If the purpose of routine screening is to uncover persons who do not know they are HIV infected, then one wonders why an upper age limit for routine screening was recommended and implemented in high-incidence areas such as New York City.

The Federal Older Americans Act, amended in 2006, states that

The Congress hereby finds and declares that, in keeping with the traditional American concept of the inherent dignity of the individual in our democratic society, the older people of our Nation are entitled to . . . (2) The best possible physical and mental health which science can make available and without regard to economic status.

Is the CDC policy of establishing an upper age limit on the public health recommendation for routine HIV screening an example of ageism and a deviation from the promises of the Older Americans Act?

The second component of the 2006 revised recommendations relates to consent and pretest counseling. Specifically, the recommendation states this:

Screening after notifying the patient that an HIV test will be performed unless the patient declines (opt-out screening) is recommended in all health-care settings. Specific signed consent for HIV testing should not be required. General informed consent for medical care should be considered sufficient to encompass informed consent for HIV testing.

The assumption underlying this policy is that a competent person is seeking the services of a healthcare provider, and those services include screening for HIV infection. An opt-out option has been defined by CDC as

Performing HIV screening after notifying the patient that 1) the test will be performed and 2) the patient may elect to decline or defer testing. Assent is inferred unless the patient declines testing.

The American Cancer Society (2008) provides an explanation of the difference between implicit and written consent. They explain that all medical care requires the patient's consent, but in cases with low risk, such as having a blood test, a simple consent is adequate. They go on to say that in cases in which there are larger possible risks, written consent is necessary. The amount of blood needed for the HIV screening is easily included in the tubes of blood routinely drawn during a visit to a healthcare facility and the amount of time that the person drawing the blood takes to fill one more tube is negligible since access has already been attained.

The CDC recommendation supports that drawing blood for HIV is a low-risk procedure and simple consent is sufficient; however, the identification of an opt-out option recognizes that this screening requires special consideration. Persons are not given an opt-out option for other screening tests such as syphilis or hereditary issues such as sickle cell or other anemia. After admission into healthcare facilities, persons sign general consent forms and then explicit consent forms for specific procedures such as surgery. In the past, HIV screening has been handled as requiring an explicit consent form. With this new recommendation, HIV screening will be transferred to the general consent for medical treatment standard. Thus, why is an opt-out option being made available? If HIV is not a special case, why are persons being alerted that they can choose not to have this specific test? If HIV is a special case, what is the rationale? Could it be that, as cited by the CDC in 2003, healthcare providers do not want to spend the time doing the necessary counseling before the testing.

If healthcare providers do not want to take the time to counsel persons about HIV infection, will they be competent to handle newly diagnosed persons with HIV infection? Some persons will be surprised and perhaps devastated at learning that they are infected. By identifying the 25% of the cases that the CDC believes are infected and unaware, will

networks of knowledgeable and sensitive healthcare providers also be identified? Will more resources be made available to stage and treat these newly diagnosed persons with HIV/AIDS? Does this public health policy focus on the needs of the group and harm the individual?

Because one of the reasons for the removal of a written consent is that healthcare providers do not have the time to counsel persons before testing for HIV, alternate methods of counseling could be developed. Persons could complete a simple true/false quiz while waiting to see the healthcare provider that addresses the key components of HIV counseling such as safer sex recommendations, the fact that HIV is a treatable condition, and that blood will be routinely tested for HIV but that clients can decline this testing. All clients would be required to complete five to six true/false questions in a format similar to that used in providing information about their health insurance. Clients would be able to review their answers with the healthcare provider and be more aware of their opt-out option, and healthcare providers would not need to spend excessive time in counseling. In situations in which computer access is available, these quizzes could be taken online and the responses made part of the client's electronic health record.

Policies related to HIV infection are often influenced more by politics and economics than public health considerations. Healthcare providers should not assume that new policies are based on sound practices but, rather, explore the motivation behind these policies, especially in situations in which marginalized populations are particularly impacted by the health issue. Healthcare providers should be vocal in their feedback about the proposed policy and provide clinical insights that might be helpful for legislators as they create laws.

Case Study Questions

In this second case, there are some very specific changes in hospital policy dealing with HIV. What are they? In what ways is the adoption and/or acceptance of those policies tied to expertise power? In the change in policy about HIV screening, what was the role of expertise, both within and beyond the medical community? How was expert knowledge balanced against our broader understanding of HIV throughout society? The expertise on these issues preceded the change in policy: what does that tell us about expertise and power?

Case Study References

American Cancer Society. (2008). *Making treatment decisions.* Retrieved May 11, 2008, from http://www.cancer.org/docroot/ETO/content/ETO_1_2X_Informed_Consent.asp

Centers for Disease Control and Prevention. (2006). Revised recommendations for HIV testing of adults, adolescents, and pregnant women in health-care settings. *Morbidity and Mortality Weekly Report, 55*(RR-14), 1–17.

Centers for Disease Control and Prevention. (2007). *Living with HIV/AIDS.* Retrieved May 11, 2008, from http://www.cdc.gov/hiv/resources/brochures/livingwithhiv.htm#q2

Centers for Disease Control and Prevention. (2008). *HIV/AIDS surveillance report, 2006.* Retrieved February 16, 2010, from http://www.cdc.gov/hiv/topics/surveillance/resources/reports

Older Americans Act Amendments of 2006. Title I—Declaration of Objectives; Definitions. Declaration of Objectives for Older Americans. Section 101. Retrieved May 11, 2008, from http://www.aoa.gov/AoARoot/AoA_Programs/OAA/oaa_full.asp

CASE STUDY

External Stakeholder Power: Successful Efforts to Pass Advanced Practice Nurse Legislation

Claudia J. Beverly

The Arkansas State Legislature meets every other year to conduct the business of the state. In the year preceding the legislative session, the Policy Committee of the Arkansas Nurses Association (ArNA) examines the healthcare needs of the state and designs a strategic health policy plan for nursing that will be introduced in the upcoming session. The work is always initiated with a clear understanding of the needs of the citizens of the State of Arkansas. In this rural state, 69 of the 75 counties are medically underserved. The poverty level is one of the worst in the country. The health statistics of Arkansans are in the bottom four states. and several counties do not have a single primary care provider. Given the many healthcare challenges facing the

state, nursing is in a key position to address these needs and is expected to do so by society.

In the early 1990s, the ArNA, which represents all nurses in Arkansas, concluded that advanced practice nurses were best prepared to address the primary healthcare needs of Arkansans. At that time, however, there was no standardization or clear regulation for this level of nurse other than national certification and the registered nurse (RN) license that is basic for all levels of registered nurses.

The ArNA's first attempt to address the primary healthcare needs of the citizens was in 1993. Their attempt to pass legislation that would allow prescriptive authority by advanced practice nurses failed. After this failure, the ArNA, with the assistance of its lobbyist, began to develop legislation to be introduced in the 1995 legislative session to provide a mechanism for advanced practice nurses to practice to the extent to which they were academically prepared. Additionally, a mechanism whereby society could be assured of safe practice by all providers needed to be in place.

The process began when a legislator from a rural area where the need was greatest introduced a "study bill." This study bill provided the opportunity for the ArNA to educate legislators about advanced practice nursing and how this type of nurse could address the healthcare needs of Arkansans. The study bill was assigned to the Interim Public Health, Welfare and Labor Committee of both the House of Representatives and the Senate. Several public hearings were held by the committee, and various groups and individuals both in support and in opposition were given the opportunity to voice their opinions.

During the hearings, there were opportunities to provide correct information supported by the literature. Clarification of the proposed legislation was also always on the agenda. At one point, concern was raised about the use of the term "collaboration with medicine," as some persons preferred to use "supervision" or a definition that would limit the practice to one being supervised. The task force initiated a process to define the term collaboration. A review of the literature showed that collaboration had already been defined in the seventies by both medicine and nursing. Armed with that information and definitions given by other sources, the task force reported their findings at the next hearing and the definition jointly developed by medicine, and nursing was incorporated in the proposed legislation.

Process for Success

The leadership of the ArNA understood the monumental task and the many challenges and barriers to addressing the healthcare needs of Arkansans. The association decided that appointing a special task force to lead its efforts was the best strategy. This strategy provided a mechanism for focusing on this issue while ensuring that the health policy committee would continue to focus on broader policy issues.

The association selected a chair, included the chair in selection of the members by ArNA leadership, and established the first meeting. As the process evolved, two co-chairs, a secretary, and a treasurer were named. The task force was representative of nursing broadly and included members of the Arkansas State Board of Nursing, master's prepared advanced practice nurses (midwives, certified registered nurse anesthetists, nurse practitioners, and clinical nurse specialists), registered nurses, faculty from schools of nursing preparing advanced practice nurses, and representatives from other nursing organizations. The task force met every other week during the first 6 months of the 2-year preparatory period and then weekly for the remaining year and a half.

The first order of business was to develop a strategic plan that included establishing a vision, mission, goals and objectives, strategies, and a time line. The vision was critical as a means of keeping task force members focused on the vast needs of Arkansans, particularly those in rural areas. The vision statement also served to keep the broader ArNA membership focused. A literature search on advanced practice nursing and health policy issues was conducted, and articles were distributed to all task force members. The assumption was that all of the members needed information to expand their current knowledge. Subcommittees were developed based on goals and objectives and the operational needs of the task force. Chairs were assigned for each subcommittee, and thus began the 2-year journey.

The American Nurses Association played a vital role in the process. The legal department was available to assemble and provide information, offer guidance, and identify potential barriers and challenges. The support provided by the ANA was pivotal to our success.

The work of the task force focused on external and internal strategies. External strategies focused on stakeholders, which included the Arkansas Medical Society and the Arkansas Medical Board and the Pharmacy Association. Understanding the views of our colleagues in other disciplines and identifying the opposition to our plans were critical to our success. Many meetings focused on educating those disciplines about the legislation we were seeking. Often this was a balancing act, providing the right information, but not too much of our strategy while attempting to keep our "enemy" close to us. We valued the process of negotiation and participated in many opportunities to negotiate with colleagues.

Throughout this process, the ArNA did have a "line in the sand," defined as the point at which there was no negotiation. Our line in the sand included regulations of advanced practice nurses by the Arkansas State Board of Nursing and reimbursement paid directly to the nurses. These two points were never resolved until a vote on the legislation occurred.

The good news is that the APN legislation passed successfully in 1995. The legislation was successful in that the criteria for an APN to be licensed in the State of Arkansas were written by nursing, APNs were to be regulated by nursing, and the legislation acknowledged national certification and educational requirements. Prescriptive authority was granted, and selected scheduled drugs could be ordered by an APN. Reimbursement to APNs was lost at the last minute. For APNs practicing in the field of geriatrics, Medicare passed reimbursement regulations in 1997. Medicaid reimburses geriatric nurse practitioners according to national guidelines. Reimbursement is critical to meeting Arkansans' needs and is a topic that is continuing to be discussed.

Many individuals participated in this successful campaign. A clear vision, legislation based on evidence and current literature, a comprehensive strategic plan, education of all parties, including those in opposition and those in support, and well-informed legislators were critical to success. Probably the most critical message in health policy legislation is to focus on the needs of the citizenry and what nursing needs to contribute.

Case Study Questions

We suspect that most nursing professionals can expand on this case; however, the key question is what is the nature of the building of a stakeholder network here? Who were the critical "first" players in this movement and why? As the network expanded, which other professional groups were involved? Why those? Do you see why some professions were the logical next parts of the coalition for adopting change? Who was most likely to oppose advanced practice nursing? Obviously, you do not include likely opponents in the initial development of the network of stakeholders, but why is that? How did the coalition eventually succeed through this inclusive network? What would you have done differently in a different practice arena? What does this case study tell you about building stakeholders for advancing practice? What would you need to do to apply this policy to advancing roles in your healthcare setting?

CASE STUDY

Internal Expertise Power: The Politics of Moving to an Electrical Medical Record

Pamela Trevino

Making significant change in an institution is a long and tedious process. It is essential to get support and buy in from all levels of the organization and often requires fancy footwork. For example, moving to an electronic medical record is a substantial process change for all who use it, and even small portions of the change can be daunting.

After learning the benefits and safety of bedside medication verification (BMV) using barcode technology, an executive safety committee at a 310-bed hospital decided to implement the technology and an electronic medication administration record. In the earliest stages of development, an executive-level committee included representatives from the following divisions: medicine (physicians), pharmacy, and nursing. They discussed the theoretical

and technological needs for the system to work within an existing technological framework and began evaluating systems.

As the executives began to evaluate the use of the system, it was decided that a front-line bedside staff member needed to be part of the decision making body, as the changes would directly affect those at the bedside. A nurse from an elite team trained to work in every hospital area was chosen to join the committee for her referent power, credibility, and knowledge of multiple hospital areas. Although the nurse was unsure about the necessity of the change, she joined the committee to represent the interests of the bedside staff. In the first weeks on the committee, the nurse was presented with the literature and evidence related to the increased safety of the barcode technology and asked to compare the new technology to the current standard of practice. As the bedside nurse became immersed in the literature, evaluated the current process, and was included in site visits, she became a strong advocate for the safety of the new technology.

As the process continued, a product was purchased, and the implementation process began. Interdisciplinary subcommittees, including all of the disciplines either affected or with a stake in the process, were formed to discuss the ways the system would change current practice. Medicine, nursing, pharmacy, respiratory therapy, information technology, quality management, billing, discharge planning, and fiscal administration were involved in building the system to meet all of the institution's needs, discuss the change in practice, and make policy and procedural changes.

To combat resistance to the product and related changes in process, the system was designed to look as much like the current paper forms as possible. A "BMV Fair" was held in which all front-line respiratory and nursing staff could see and use the technology prior to the official education and implementation. Staff members were encouraged to give feedback on the product, ways to improve the process, and their personal opinions of the technology. The system was then evaluated and changed to accommodate staff preferences where possible, to help remove barriers to acceptance, although the system was still not popular among front-line staff.

The "BMV Fair" also brought to the forefront the lack of basic computer skills in some members of the team. A basic computer competency was developed for all front-line staff members, and classes were offered for those team members who did possess basic computer skills. Staff members were advised early that they would be expected to be able to use the system, and they would not be allowed to work if they could not use the computer-based medication system.

With the move to computer-based charting, computers needed to be available at every bedside. Because of the diversity of the hospital, all units were asked to determine whether they would like mounted computers in every room or computers on wheels (COWs) that could be moved throughout a unit. Because patient rooms are fairly busy, all of the units decided on COWs because of their mobility and flexibility. Each unit was able to borrow several different models and "test drive" them in their area. Nurses were encouraged to give their feedback and suggestions to the purchasing team, and then to decide on a COW. Interestingly, all of the units chose the same COW, which then could be maintained in a central location by information technology personnel.

As the go-live dates approached, training was developed and taught by a member of the information technology staff with a nursing background and by the original bedside nurse on the committee. The bedside nurse shared her initial hesitancy to adopt the system as well as her change to advocacy. Because the institution had a culture geared toward patient safety, front-line staff were told that the process would feel clumsy and take longer initially than current practice but in the end would be safer for the patient. The education highlighted those things that had been added into the system for the convenience of the front-line staff, such as customized computers on wheels, the system "extras" that would save time and effort, and area-specific ways to incorporate the system into everyday practice. Because the hospital chose a staggered roll out, education for each area was held in the 2 weeks before the go-live date. Area-specific questions and concerns were anticipated and addressed with each class.

Within 30 minutes of going live, the system caught the first medication error. Initially, the staff member believed that the system was not working correctly but then learned that the system was correct and that he was attempting to give the wrong medication. This initial user became a strong advocate for the system, and without giving specifics, the information was shared with each subsequent group during their education to show the validity of the system. As more units began using the system, more events occurred, and the information was shared with all the staff members in the hospital. A centralized e-mail account was set up to allow staff to share successes, suggest improvements, and ask questions and feel they were part of the ongoing process.

The implementation was surprisingly smooth, and the system has become part of the culture of the hospital. There are still several committees related to different aspects of the system that meet on a regular basis to address issues that were not foreseeable during the original implementation; however, through careful planning, politics, and change agents, the implementation and enculturation have been a definite success.

Case Study Questions

Based on what you just read, what is the expertise being developed here? What is the challenge to others accepting this expertise? What is it in this case that indicates acceptance of the expertise? What were challenges? What role does process play in making changes such as these? Is there a danger that electronic records will define the questions rather than those involved in direct care?

CASE STUDY

Expanding Newborn Screening in Arkansas
Ralph Vogel

Advances in technology have created great advances in how we can provide services to families and their children. A prime example of this is the expansion of newborn screening, which has dramatically increased the number and type of genetic conditions that can be detected immediately after birth. Historically, most states have screened for hemoglobinopathies (like sickle cell anemia), thyroid, phenylketonuria, and galactosemia. These conditions, along with newborn hearing screening, were relatively easy to assess at a cost effective rate. With advanced laboratory and computer technology, we can now add multiple genetic conditions that are identified during a single run. In 2004, the March of Dimes proposed expanding the genetic conditions for which newborns are screened to their "List of 29," including several enzyme deficiency conditions and cystic fibrosis. The cost of the limited newborn screening was approximately $15 per newborn, and this would rise to about $90 with the expanded list. Insurance companies would cover the cost of adding the additional conditions. The value of newborn screening is in identifying genetic conditions early and implementing treatment plans from birth. Over the life span, this greatly reduces the morbidity and mortality associated with later diagnosis. With some conditions, the care can be as simple as a dietary change that is implemented from birth. Early diagnosis also allows for genetic counseling with families about the risk that additional children will have the condition.

Many states adopted this recommendation quickly, although the process has been slower in others. In Arkansas, a committee, titled the Arkansas Genetics Health Advisory Committee (formerly Service), has existed for several years. Their mission is to monitor health care related to genetics in the state. This diverse committee includes several members of the Arkansas Department of Health (ADH) involved in the newborn screening program administration and laboratory testing, the physicians from Arkansas Children's Hospital genetic clinic, and interested parties that either work in the area of genetics or are parents of children with genetic conditions.

The main purpose of the committee has been to coordinate care and to try to educate the public about genetic conditions and screening for newborns. The ADH receives samples from about 95% of the newborns in the state and does screening at their central location in Little Rock. When an infant is identified with a newborn genetic condition, the ADH then notifies the community hospital and the assigned pediatrician, who does the counseling with the family and develops a plan for care and follow-up.

Expanding the screening program to the existing March of Dimes List of 29 created several problems.

The committee, however, felt strongly that it should take an advocacy role to address these concerns. The first problem was the cost of increased screening. Although most of the individual cost for each child could be absorbed by insurance or Medicaid reimbursement, as in other states, the initial financial support would need to be provided by the state. The ADH had no provision for increasing funding but estimated that the increased cost would be as follows:

- Two million dollars for equipment and supplies
- The addition of at least two more laboratory technicians to do the increased testing
- The addition of at least one more public health nurse to coordinate the increased number of identified genetic cases
- Training for new and current personnel on the new equipment
- Personnel time to develop and coordinate the expansion of the program
- Development of an education program to make parents and professionals aware of the changes

Overall, the estimated cost for startup was approximately $3 million, some of which could be recouped after billing for the tests was established.

The committee and ADH decided that we would outline a plan for expansion with estimated costs and submit it to the director of the ADH, Dr. Faye Bozeman. With his approval, we would then approach legislators and ask for the needed funding to be included in the upcoming budget. Because the state legislature for Arkansas only convened every 2 years, it would be critical to move forward over the next 6 months. We prepared a letter to Dr. Bozeman that the committee approved on a Friday with the intention of mailing it on the following Monday. On the next day, Saturday, Dr. Bozeman was killed in an accident on his farm; therefore, we were in a quandary about who should receive the letter and whose approval would be needed in the ADH. Over the next 6 months, there was an interim head who was thrust into the position and did not want to approve anything at this level of expense. Basically, we were on hold until a permanent director was named. After about 3 months, we decided to take another tack and develop a plan to seek legislative approval for funding and then approach the new ADH director after the person was named. We developed a list of legislators to contact and identified members of the committee who had worked with the legislators in the past and could approach them.

By this time, we were 2 months from the legislature convening and knew that once it convened nothing new would be introduced; therefore, we had to get support before their convening. We approached some legislators and received tacit support, but none was willing to introduce a new bill or request funding at this time without a permanent head of ADH. We had lost the opportunity for funding until the next legislative session in 2 years.

The committee decided to continue to seek support from the legislators and ADH with the idea of gaining funding in 2 years. Meanwhile, we began to look at other states and what newborn screenings they were currently doing to make sure that politicians were aware of national standards. We had identified that Arkansas was one of the last five states to not expand newborn screening, and all of the surrounding states in the region had incorporated all or a large part of the March of Dimes List of 29. Making legislators aware of this became one of our goals, and once they realized that the states surrounding Arkansas were already doing expanded screening of newborns, they were more receptive to our plan.

After we started to discuss funding with legislators during the legislative session, they seemed willing to support newborn screening; however, then we had a surprise: They stated that it did not require any special legislation or special funding. They stated that the ADH could expand newborn screening without their approval because this was already within their realm of responsibility. Funding could be obtained by submitting a budget request to cover the cost of expansion.

The interim head of ADH was willing to support this since the head of the newborn screening section, was on our committee. By fall, we had the budget expansion approved and support for newborn screening expansion. The decision was then made to target July 1, 2008, as the date for starting the expanded program.

After we knew that the finances and political support were confirmed, we developed a timeline that involved acquisition of the equipment, training for ADH staff, an education program for the public, and a plan for making community hospitals and professional healthcare providers aware of the expansion. At this point, the ADH contacted members of the media that it had worked with in the past and developed a plan for public information advertisements to be run on television and radio. These began running in early May, 2 months before the July 1 start date. Because the media members had worked with ADH in the past, it was much easier to develop the advertisements. Print media advertisements were also started, and the local chapter of the March of Dimes provided funding and brochures that were distributed to OB/GYN physicians in the state to make expectant mothers aware of the testing to be done on their newborns. One of the members of the committee also wrote an article that appeared in the March issue of the *Arkansas State Board of Nursing Update* magazine, which is distributed to 40,000 healthcare providers in the state.

In July, the expanded screening was begun, and it has been continued with a relatively smooth transition, largely because of the preparation of the ADH staff in the laboratory and the outreach nurses. Because of the public awareness campaign, there has been little voiced concern from parents, and there seems to be an awareness of the value of the expanded screening.

Lessons learned from the process are these:

- Preparation is the key to a smooth transition.
- Know exactly what is required to proceed and who needs to approve new or expanded plans of action. If we had approached the legislature first to find out what they wanted, we could have saved time.
- Plan for the unexpected. We could not have anticipated Dr. Bozeman's death, but it did cause about a 6-month delay.
- Educate everyone who is going to be involved. This includes administrators, healthcare providers, laboratory staff, parents, and professionals in the communities impacted.
- Discuss with the media exactly what they need and use their expertise in terms of length of announcements and the best ways to distribute information.

Although the entire process took over 2 years, in the end, the transition has been very smooth, and few problems have been identified at any level. Having a diverse group on the committee was a strength because different members had different perspectives. This gave us much greater ability to anticipate problems and coordinate care, and in the end, the program in place will benefit newborns in Arkansas for years to come.

Case Study Questions

This case is a good example of how the stakeholders adapted as the intended policy change moved from internal adoption of policy to legislation back to internal adoption of policy within an existing organization. Can you see how the nature of the stakeholders defined for a legislative change is different from stakeholders for an adaptation of existing policy? The initial group involved in this process was established primarily as an informational group but changed to one advocating change. How did the group evolve to influence policy differently? If the initial group had been more broadly defined at the start, would it have made the same mistake about requiring legislative change to adopt the policy? Why or why not?

Final Case Study

This final case study is presented to stimulate the reader's political thinking. We encourage you to read the case carefully and then consider how you would go about creating an environment for policy change.

CASE STUDY

Workplace Violence

Steven L. Baumann and Eileen Levy

In the wake of the terrorist attack of September 11, 2001, and a series of tragic school shootings, workplace violence has gained national attention in the United States. Although nurses and other healthcare workers are generally well educated and regularly reminded to practice good hand washing and infection control, there is little attention given to the potential for violence in hospitals and other healthcare settings, even though it is common and can have devastating long-term consequences (Department of Health and Human Services, 2002; U.S. Department of Labor, 2004). According to Love and Morrison (2003), nurses who sustain injuries from patient assaults, in addition to suffering psychological trauma, are often out of work for periods of time, have financial problems, show decreased work productivity, make more errors at work, and report a decreased desire to remain a nurse. In addition to these problems, nurses who have been assaulted report feeling less able to provide appropriate care to their patients (Farrell et al., 2006) and are reluctant to make formal complaints (Love & Morrison, 2003). As was the case with needle stick injuries in the past, many organizations do not openly discuss organizational problems that increase the risk for violence, nor do they adequately prepare for episodes of violence, leaving nurses more likely to blame themselves for its occurrence.

The National Institute for Occupational Safety and Health (NIOSH), the same organization that requires hospitals to be attentive to infection control strategies and proper handling of hazardous materials, also provides clear definitions and guidelines to reduce the potential for violence in the workplace. According NIOSH, workplace violence includes acts of physical violence or threats of violence directed toward people on duty or at work (Department of Health and Human Services, 2002). NIOSH has recognized employer responsibilities in mitigating workplace violence and assisting employees who are victims (Love & Morrison, 2003). The U.S. government has required employers to provide safe workplaces since 1970 (U.S. Department of Labor, 2004). These federal guidelines call for hospitals and other organizations to incorporate written programs to assure job safety and security into the overall safety and health program for their facilities. Violence prevention, they suggest, needs to have administrative commitment and employee involvement.

This case study is of a moderate-sized, nonprofit community hospital in the New York Metropolitan area. As in many parts of the United States, this hospital and the communities it serves are becoming increasingly crowded and diverse. In this environment of change and tension, the hospital is a meeting place of people, many not by choice but in crisis, bringing together dramatically different histories, backgrounds, educational attainment, and cultures. The hospital and its clinics have become increasingly stressful, unpredictable, and at times hostile places. For example, the use of hospitals as holding tanks for acutely disturbed and violent individuals, the release of mentally ill persons from public hospitals without adequate outpatient programs and follow-up services, and the accessibility of handguns and drugs in communities all contribute to hospital and community violence. A failure of leadership at various levels, as well as inadequate reimbursement from payers, has contributed to violence that can occur on its premises.

The case study hospital, like most in the United States, has dramatically reduced the number of public psychiatric beds. Many of these former psychiatric patients have to rely on outpatient mental health services supported by community hospitals with a limited number of beds on one or two psychiatric units. In addition, the case study hospital reduced inpatient and outpatient addiction services. New research suggests that actively psychotic patients with schizophrenia and patients with schizophrenia who had a premorbid conduct problem or exposure to violence are more likely to be violent than less acutely ill patients and those without substance abuse or antisocial personality co-morbidity (Swanson et al., 2008). Nevertheless, it is a mistake to consider persons with mental illness or substance abuse as the only individuals who can become agitated or violent in healthcare settings. It is also shortsighted to solely blame any single policy, such as the deinstitutionalization of the chronically mentally ill, for workplace violence in the United States.

At the same time that the case study hospital has cut beds and programs for persons in distress, the case study hospital has a clear mission/vision/value statement that puts professional nurses in leadership positions and has taken steps to address workplace violence. It has made efforts to reduce violence in high-risk areas, such as the emergency department and psychiatric unit by restricting access to these areas, using surveillance equipment, panic buttons, and a strict requirement for all staff to wear identification, as other hospitals have. Community hospitals, like the one in this case study, however, often do not provide the kind of ongoing self-defense and violence prevention education and training that many psychiatric hospitals provide. In addition, all hospitals should have a task force and regularly meeting committee consisting of management, human resources/employee relations, employee assistance program staff, security and the office of chief counsel with the sole purpose of developing policies and procedures to prevent and address workplace violence.

Following The Joint Commission's (2008) lead, the case study hospital and nursing administration have hospital wide discussions and training on "behaviors that undermine a culture of safety." In addition, the hospital requires workplace violence risk assessment, hazard prevention and control, and safety and health training, as well as careful record keeping and program evaluation (U.S. Department of Labor, 2004). Hospitals need to keep in mind the malpractice crisis in this country. The move to put patients first does not turn over control of the hospital to patients or their families. Indeed, to understand Friedman (2007) correctly, in order to put patients' health and satisfaction first, the hospital needs effective leadership at the top and from its professional nurses. To prevent violence in the workplace, nurses need to strive to be as authentic in their patient contact as possible and to avoid detached impersonal interactions (Carlsson et al., 2006). The case study hospital provides considerable avenues of reward for individual nurses and other staff members to advance themselves and stand out as innovative, which helps mitigate the tendency for workers to "herd," to use Friedman's (2007) term—that is to say, to avoid developing themselves and improving the institution for the sake of togetherness with selected coworkers.

The case study hospital does provide a psychiatric nurse practitioner on staff and onsite one day a week as an employee assistance provider. Having this person onsite provides an opportunity for hospital staff to have counseling to become less reactive to emotionally intense environments, as recommended by Friedman (2007). Healthcare organizations also need to provide referral information such as employee assistance program or clinicians experienced in trauma care for employees who may exhibit more serious and persistent reactions to perceived violence and aggression (Bernstein & Saladino, 2007). Nurses and nursing organizations should become more familiar with national guidelines and recommendations and persuade their hospitals to adopt and implement them. The process for nurses is to focus more on taking responsibility for their own condition, practice self-regulation, and have a wide repertory of responses to stressful situations. Although this does not guarantee that violence will be avoided, it does make it less likely to happen and makes nurses better able to keep it in perspective. Friedman (2007) described this as being able to turn down the dial or volume. Nurses need to be just as effective in managing "toxic" emotional environments, as in handling toxic chemicals and infections. Nurses' interpersonal effectiveness is increased when they look for and support strengths in others. Postincident debriefing helps transform the experience into a team building and learning opportunity. Leaders should involve all staff and review events, including what precedes and follows an incident.

Case Study Conclusion

A community hospital in the New York metropolitan area is presented as a case study of an organization struggling to carry out its mission in a way that facilitates the growth and well-being of its employees. The hospital is experiencing different pulls. On the one hand it has had to cut back on essential programs. On the other hand, the nurses and the central leadership in the hospital need to work together to avoid quick-fix solutions and suffer the failure of nerve that Friedman (2007) talked about. The busy hospital environment in a changing society is stressful and at times a hostile and violent one. Nurses need to be effective leaders to help protect the integrity of the hospital as an organization—that is to say maintain its self-definition. They can best do this by becoming as self-defined as they can and

by consistently implementing federal guidelines to prevent and manage workplace violence.

Case Study Questions

In this last case you have a need for policy change—which we suspect is a need in many healthcare organizations—the need for workplace violence policies. Here is our challenge to the reader. Can you take our two components, both an internal and external role, and define what needs to be done to accomplish this policy change? We suggest that you define the work in terms of your most likely environment, whether a psychiatric facility or a hospital or clinic. How would you go about creating an environment for policy change here?

Some core questions should guide you. First, what key stakeholders are in the initial stakeholder group (i.e., those most likely to feel the strongest need for the policy)? Are they organized around various professional lines within your organization? How do you begin to create a networked shared view among these stakeholders? As you begin to broaden the network, which groups should be brought into the discussion? Let us give you an example: The human resource specialists in your organization will need to be involved at some point in creating a policy about the elimination/reduction of workplace violence. Should they, however, be in your initial set of stakeholders? Why or why not?

Now . . . the more difficult question: What is the expertise needed to make such a policy change? What are the kind of facts (someone has to gather the data in a systematic way), that need to be gathered? Are we discussing violence between patients and those providing medical services, or are we also talking about violence between fellow professionals within the organization? What kind of violence/danger are we discussing here—physical or verbal violence or both? What about safety issues (including other types of danger to employees and patients)? Would you agree that an emergency room might see these questions a bit differently from those handling financial claims (although both have real needs here)? How do you build expert power here? Who shares it, and who might be expert in defining these issues over time?

Case Study References

Bernstein, K. S., & Saladino, J. P. (2007). Clinical assessment and management of psychiatric patients' violent and aggressive behaviors in general hospital. *Medsurg Nursing, 16,* 301–309.

Carlsson, G., Dahlberg, K., Ekcbergh, M., & Dahlberg, H. (2006). Patients longing for authentic personal care: A phenomenological study of violent encounters in psychiatric settings. *Issues in Mental Health Nursing, 27,* 287–305.

Department of Health and Human Services. (2002). *Violence: Occupational hazards in hospitals.* Centers for Disease Control and Prevention/National Institute for Occupational Safety and Health. Document # 2002-101. Cincinnati, OH: National Institute for Occupational Safety and Health.

Farrell, G. A., Bobrowski, C., & Bobrowski, P. (2006). Scoping workplace aggression in nursing: findings from an Australian study. *Journal of Advanced Nursing, 55,* 778–787.

Friedman, E. H. (2007). *A failure of nerve: Leadership in the age of the quick fix.* New York: Seabury (originally published in 1999).

Love, C. C., & Morrison, E. (2003). American Academy of Nursing expert panel on violence policy recommendation on workplace violence (adopted 2002). *Issues in Mental Health Nursing, 24,* 599–604.

Swanson, J. W., Van Dorn, R. A., Swartz, M. S., Smith, M., Elbogen, E. B., & Monahan, J. (2008). Alternative Pathways to Violence in Persons with Schizophrenia. *The Role of Childhood Antisocial Behavior, 32*(3), 228–240.

The Joint Commission. (July, 2008). Behaviors that undermine a culture of safety. Retrieved February 2, 2009, from http://www.jointcommission.org/SentinelEventAlert/sea_40.htm

U.S. Department of Labor. (2004). *Guidelines for preventing workplace violence for health care & social service workers* (OSHA 3148-01R). Washington, DC: Occupational Safety and Health Administration.

Chapter Conclusion

This book on politics and policy requires an understanding of how to build support and adapt to change. If we are to be effective advocates, we must be responsive to broader societal needs. Building support is not done simply by presenting the facts. This toolkit is designed to help readers know what it takes in a political environment to build a case and adapt when necessary. A huge mistake in advocacy is to simply believe that the facts are on our side, and if we just continue to list the facts, everyone will believe! In reality, values and political issues are at the core of successful change. Our tasks as political advocates for change are to:

1. Believe we can convince others to adapt
2. Adapt ourselves to handle broader political value issues
3. Learn to mobilize our expert power as one of the largest group of stakeholders in the healthcare field

Chapter References

Fottler, M. D., Blair, J. D., Whitehead, C. J., Laus, M. D., & Savage, G. T. (1989). Assessing key stakeholders: Who matters to hospitals and why? *Hospitals and Health Services Administration, 34*(4), 525–546.

Wilson, J. Q. (1989). *Bureaucracy: What government agencies do and why they do it.* New York: Basic Books.

Foreword

Diana J. Mason, PhD, RN, FAAN
Editor-in-Chief
American Journal of Nursing

By all accounts, Julie Thao was an excellent, veteran obstetrics nurse, yet her decisions on July 4 and 5, 2006, led to the death of Jasmine Gant, a 16-year-old laboring woman; the loss of her job; the loss of her license; and a felony charge for "criminal neglect of a patient causing great bodily harm" that later was reduced to two misdemeanors. Her errors included:

- Not ensuring that the patient had the regulation, bar-coded wristband in place
- Failing to use the 3-week-old medication bar-coding system that could have alerted her to the fact that she was about to give Gant an unordered epidural (bupivacaine) medication instead of IV penicillin
- Failing to review the five rights of medication administration before giving the wrong medication the wrong route (bupivacaine IV)

Why would a veteran nurse make such decisions?

Thao's worst decision was the one she made on July 4 to work a double shift, sleep for less than 8 hours at the hospital, and then work another shift. When she made the errors, she had worked about 20 hours in a 28-hour period. We know that fatigue is associated with an increased risk of errors; that too many nurses are working too many hours, impairing their judgment, and putting the lives and well-being of their patients in jeopardy (Rogers, Hwang, Scott, Aiken, & Dinges, 2004; Trinkoff, Geiger-Brown, Brady, Lipscomb, & Muntaner, 2006).

Perhaps she agreed to work these hours because she wasn't aware of this literature that documents an increased risk of errors once one exceeds 12 hours in a 24-hour period. Too many nurses believe that their education stops with the original program that led to their license—they don't pursue higher degrees or even read nursing journals (Mason, 2007a; Bevill, Lacey, & Cleary, 2007)—raising questions about the meaning of "informed" decision-making.

Or maybe she thought herself invulnerable. She probably had worked many double shifts in her 16 years of nursing practice—and I've argued elsewhere (Mason, 2007b) that Thao was probably seen as a "good" nurse—the one who will do those double shifts when the hospital is understaffed. I don't know Julie Thao but she may come from a family or culture that values a work ethic in which one should go to whatever lengths necessary to be the "good" (translated, compliant, and unchallenging) employee.

However, to put the blame of the errors on the shoulders of Julie Thao is a disservice to her and to the memory of Jasmine Gant. Thao and nurses like her are working in systems that too often fail to value nursing care as the core business of institutions. People rarely become patients in hospitals if they don't need nursing care. Despite a substantial and growing body of research documenting the link between nurse staffing and both clinical and financial outcomes of care, hospitals and other health care organizations continue to expect nurses to care for too many patients and fail to put into place the policies and systems that will catch the errors that all of us make ("to err is human") and support thoughtful decision-making by frontline clinicians. Hospitals may ignore the research on nurse staffing while investing in expensive, high-tech diagnostic equipment, for example. In a provocative editorial in Nursing Research, Blegen (2006) challenges us to carefully examine the decisions that are being made in the name of patient safety and quality improvement. For example, she notes that hospitals and other health care facilities are paying for expensive, high-tech solutions to patient safety such as bar-coding systems while failing to pay for the systems and support necessary for collecting standardized data on nurse-sensitive outcomes or investing in improving communication among providers or with patients that could markedly reduce errors and improve the quality of care.

Health care organizations are run by people who are making decisions that can either cultivate or undermine conditions and systems that are conducive to safe, humane care. Why does a chief nurse officer (CNO) fail to advocate for better staffing when she or he knows that poor staffing can lead to a higher rate of deaths and complications, as well as be costly? Why does the CNO staff the hospital or home care agency by expecting or mandating overtime from existing staff? Why does the chief executive officer (CEO) expect the CNO to staff at current levels despite the increased acuity of patients and higher census? Why does the CEO think it is more important to invest in high-tech diagnostic equipment than in nursing personnel? Why does the chief medical officer insist on putting into place "rapid response" teams to try to reduce cardiac arrests and morality instead of insisting on adequate staffing and staff development to prevent the need for such teams (Winters, Pham, & Pronovost, 2006)?

Administrators struggle with such decisions for a variety of reasons, but chief among them are decisions made by policy makers. Why do Medicare and private insurers pay for disease diagnosis and treatment but lump nursing care into room charges, putting nurses at a distinct disadvantage when trying to make the business case for better staffing (Welton, 2006; Welton, Zone-Smith, & Fischer, 2006)? Why are policy makers talking only about how to cover the uninsured by finding ways to extend payment for current models of health care rather than thinking about providing all people with a model of care that focuses on prevention, health promotion, and the patient's and family's goals and priorities for care, as already exists in hospice and palliative care?

Current practice and policy decisions of nurses, administrators, and policy makers are grounded in history, as is noted in this book. For example, in Chapter 2, Lewenson writes about the historic dominance of medicine to the extent that nursing knowledge was obscured until Lavinia Dock wrote about uniquely nursing practices. Today's nurses continue to struggle with medical dominance; a dominance that was codified when the first medical practice acts were written. These acts included a scope of practice for physicians that covered all of health care, leaving nurses and other providers to continually fight to carve out legal scopes of practice that enable them to provide care without physician supervision (Safriet, 1994). Thus, we make decisions that reflect an insecurity about our right and ability to own our knowledge, even when it might benefit patients.

In an era of evidence-based practice, we often assume that the "evidence" is truth and can guide our practice. However, Ioannidis (2005) and others (Deyo, Psaty, Simon, Wagner, & Omenn, 1997) have argued that even the decisions of researchers about what to study and how to study it can be manipulated by funders and other groups that may have a vested in the outcomes of the research, as well as the researcher's own aspirations. "Publish or perish" becomes an academic albatross when journals are reluctant to publish studies that fail to find positive results, leading some researchers to commit fraud and scientific misconduct. Furthermore, what high level of evidence for practice do we have? Funding for nursing research pales beside the funding of the pharmaceutical industry and even the National Institutes of Health (NIH). In 2006, the National Institute for Nursing Research received a paltry $137 million out of a budget of $28.8 billion for all of the NIH. This is yet another example of the importance of public policy to nurses' clinical decision-making. If clinicians are expected to engage in evidence-based practice, what happens to clinical decision-making when the only available randomized clinical trials are of pharmaceutical interventions for conditions or health problems that nursing experiences indicate are responsive to nonpharmaceutical approaches? These issues and questions suggest that nurses must be thoughtful about their reliance on "evidence-based" guidelines for care and be critical consumers of research and other "best practice" evidence.

While each of us has a responsibility to make thoughtful decisions about the care we're providing to patients and their families, we also must make thoughtful decisions and speak out about the larger issues and policies that shape the context in which our decisions are make. We must examine why we are content to be invisible within our institutions and in society. Why do we speak out-or not-about poor or unsafe working conditions? Why do we continue to work in institutions that we know are unsafe? The decision to speak out or to walk out is itself worthy of examination by each of us. What is our comfort level with living up to the advocacy role almost all nurses espouse? If we're uncomfortable with challenging the status quo and leading change, why? In this book, Elizabeth Furlong suggests that nurses ask themselves, "How did I spend my time?"; "Did I spend it justly?"; and "Is it just (to patients and to oneself) to continue working in an environment where there is consistent mandatory overtime?"

In Chapter 4 of this book, Joy Buck tells the story of Kate, who left hospital practice because her staff colleagues refused to respect the wishes of a patient and his wife at the end of life. I was moved by this story of one nurse fighting a whole system of values and priorities that resulted in care that was inhumane. Buck speaks about the moral distress that such situations create in nurses who know there is a better way to care but suppress their own and nursing's values to survive in systems that are dominated by an ethic of cure at the expense of an ethic of care. Still, nurses such as Kate beginning to refuse to tolerate systems of care in which such moral distress is rampant and unaddressed. The nursing shortage is created in part by a failure of an ethic of care to prevail in our health care organizations and to be supported by public policies that support professional caregiving.

There are hospitals and home care agencies and long-term care facilities and schools and ambulatory care centers that provide supportive work environments and excellent, safe systems of care that are truly family and patient centered. They are headed by visionary, thoughtful decision-makers who support the development and implementation of thoughtful decision-making by their staff. These are proactive, risk-taking innovators who relish the challenge of making decisions that are in the best interests of the people they serve, whether staff or patients. We all need to learn from such role models of excellent decision-making and to examine our own decisions that support either the spread of such centers of excellence or the perpetuation of mediocrity and outright bad, unsafe care.

We are all Julie Thao. We make decisions that aren't always logical or beneficial to ourselves or our patients despite our best intentions. We are products of our own genetic make up, familial values, cultural and sociopolitical contexts, and historical precedent—but perhaps we can make better decisions if we reflect on how and why we make decisions. This book provides nurses with a guide for examining who we are, some of the contextual factors that shape our decision-making, and the role of public policy in macro-level decision-making. I was stunned by Lewenson's and Truglio-Londrigan's revelation in the preface that there have been no other books examining nurses' decision-making. *Decision-Making in Nursing: Thoughtful Approaches for Practice* is long overdue. I hope it will serve as a foundation for future works and will help each of us to examine why we make the decisions we do—whether in service to our individual patients, our workplaces, our society, or ourselves.

References

Bevill, J., Lacey, L., & Cleary, B. (2007). Educational mobility of RNs in North Carolina: Who will teach tomorrow's nurses? *American Journal of Nursing, 107*(5), 60–70.

Blegen, M. (2006). Safety of healthcare: An amazing possibility. *Nursing Research, 55*(5), 299.

Deyo, R.A., Psaty, B.M., Simon, G., Wagner, E.H., & Omenn, G.S. (1997). The messenger under attack-Intimidation of researchers by special-interest groups. *New England Journal of Medicine, 336*(16), 1176–1180.

Ioannidis, J. (2005). Contradicted and initially stronger effects in highly cited clinical research. *Journal of the American Medical Association, 294*(2), 218–228.

Mason, D. J. (2007a). Which nurse do you want? *American Journal of Nursing,* 107(5), 11.

Mason, D. J. (2007b). Good nurse-Bad nurse: Is it an error or crime? *American Journal of Nursing,* 107(3), 11.

Rogers, A.E., Hwang, W.T., Scott, L.D., Aiken, L.H., & Dinges, D.F. (2004). The working hours of hospital staff nurses and patient safety. *Health Affairs,* 23(4), 202–212.

Safriet, B. (1994). Impediments to progress in health care workforce policy: License and practice laws. *Inquiry,* 31(30), 310–317.

Trinkoff, A., Geiger-Brown, J., Brady, B., Lipscomb, J., Muntaner, C. (2006). How long and how much are nurses now working? *American Journal of Nursing,* 106(4), 60–71.

Welton, J. (2006). Paying for nursing care in hospitals. *American Journal of Nursing,* 106(11), 67–69.

Welton, J.M., Zone-Smith, L., & Fischer, M.H. (2006). Adjustment of inpatient care reimbursement for nursing intensity. *Policy, Politics, and Nursing Practice,* 7(4), 270–280.

Winters, B., Pham, J., & Pronovost, P. (2006). Rapid response teams-Walk, don't run. *Journal of the American Medical Association,* 296(13), 1645–1647.

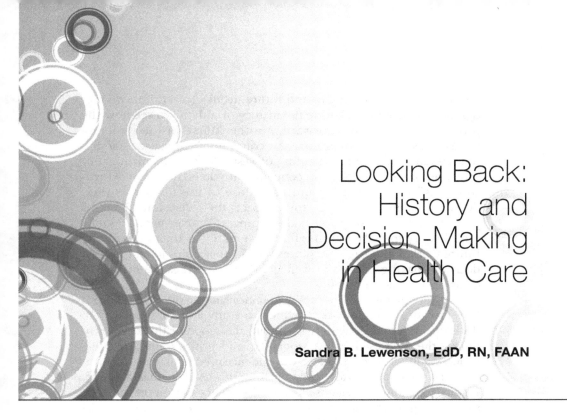

Looking Back: History and Decision-Making in Health Care

Sandra B. Lewenson, EdD, RN, FAAN

Nurses make decisions every day that affect the health of the individuals, families, and communities they serve. They make decisions about the use of clinical interventions, the use of their political vote, the education of nurses, the application of new technologies, and a myriad of others as well—yet when nurses make decisions, they often use decision-making frameworks that do not take into account past practices. Nelson and Gordon (2004) write about the "rhetoric of rupture," stating that nurses often discard and distance themselves from their past, leaving huge gaps in their knowledge. Nurses continually reinvent themselves and their practice at the expense of their history. Without understanding and valuing past contributions to practice or to society, nurses contribute to the "nursism" or bias toward the caring role that pervades this society (Lewenson, 1993). The omission of what nurses do on a day-to-day basis is lost to both current and future generations of nurses and to others who might benefit from such knowledge.

In 1939, nurse historian Mary Roberts wrote that "trends and events of today are the results of past experience as well as of varying conceptions of both present and future needs" (p. 1). Roberts recognized the need to examine the history of nursing to see how the profession could move forward. Another nurse historian Teresa Christy (1978) explained how she could not "emphasize enough the relevance of an understanding of yesterday's problems for illumination of today's issues and concomitant potential for tomorrow's solutions" (p. 5).Whether nurses choose to use history in their decision-making process, history impacts their decisions. Thus, as part of a reflective decision-making process, nurses need to know their history to make meaningful decisions about their current and future work. This chapter explores why history helps nurses in their decision-making process as well as briefly describes the history of decision-making in nursing.

Historiography provides a way of understanding the past and therefore provides a framework in which to study and apply history to decision-making. Although it is beyond the scope of this chapter to discuss the steps used in historiography, it identifies some of the historical studies that contribute to the evidence used in practice and professional growth. The case study opening this chapter illustrates how graduate nursing students use historical evidence to support the decision-making process in a community health clinical experience. The historiographies presented in this chapter offer examples of how history informs the decision-making efforts of nurses. The case study closing this chapter provides an illustration of how historical knowledge about nursing roles would help current nurses in their practice.

Case Study

A Community Assessment of the Lower East Side of New York City, 1893

What began as a study to look at the Lower East Side of New York City as Lillian Wald may have seen it when she established the Henry Street Settlement became an exciting exercise for students to explore how decisions were made. Nurses need to be able to assess a community and determine the types of services that would most benefit the community. To teach nurses how to assess a community, prioritize primary health care needs of the community, plan and develop an appropriate intervention, and examine the impact of their decisions, a look at historical data was used. In this case study, graduate nursing students interested in community and the Henry Street Settlement in the Lower East Side of New York City joined in doing a historical community assessment as part of their requirement for a master's project. To complete this requirement, they examined the period of time in which the Henry Street Settlement house was first organized.

The Henry Street Settlement was started in 1893 by two public health nurses, Lillian Wald and her friend, Mary Brewster. Using the demographic data, photographs, and selected writings from 1893 enabled the current students to more fully understand what Wald and Brewster might have seen when they first established the nurses' settlement house on the Lower East Side of New York. The study helped students learn why Wald and Brewster opened a nurses' settlement house in the area, the kinds of health care issues that they found, and the impact that their nursing decisions had on the health of that community. In addition, this project enabled students to look at the professional and health care issues over time and see how they compared with those of today. They used history to help them understand the role of the visiting nurse, the political activism that the nurses exhibited, and the obligation to society that nurses continue to maintain now in the twenty-first century. They also used their findings to help them in making decisions about community health initiatives in the same community over 100 years later.

Students studied the Lower East Side community, specifically the area designated as the 7th and 10th Ward. In the late nineteenth century, New York City was divided into wards rather than the present-day census tracts, and data was therefore collected according to ward and sanitary districts. The students examined the demographics; morbidity and mortality rates; immigration patterns; police, fire, and sanitation support services; educational, religious, and social institutions in the community; and the political and nursing issues of that period. Students identified the priority needs in the community and compared their ideas with the actual contributions of the nurses at Henry Street. The students learned about the overcrowded living conditions that so many of the immigrants who populated the Lower East Side found in the tenements. In 1893 the total population in Manhattan (a borough of New York City in which the Lower East Side was a small section) totaled 1,758,000. About 1,332,773 or 69 percent of the total population, however, lived in the tenements of the Lower East Side. There were 180,359 children under the age of 5 (*Annual Report*, 1909).

The data showed that the residents of the Lower East Side came from Italy, Germany, Hungary, Russia, and other European countries. Once they arrived in the United States and moved to the Lower East Side, they found the tenements waiting for them. They experienced six-floor walk-up apartments, a lack of running water (this was prior to the cold-water flats that evolved following the inclusion of sinks in the tenements), outdoor plumbing until plumbing moved onto the hallway of each floor, as well as poor ventilation and poor lighting. Families, regardless of their size, resided in the two rooms that made up the apartments of the early tenements. Lack of privacy was just one of the many insults to the human condition that existed for those who lived in the tenements. The Tenement Museum in New York shows what life in the tenements was like and students were able to access the Web site (www.tenement.org) as well as personally visit this setting.

The inadequate housing conditions as well as the inhumane work conditions of so many of the immigrants contributed to the poor health conditions that they experienced. Some of the findings showed that infants accounted for 25 percent of all deaths in the community and that children under 5 accounted for 40 percent of all deaths in the community. The top causes of death in 1893 were pneumonia, phthis (pulmonary tuberculosis), digestive organ diseases, heart disease, and diphtheria. Infectious diseases made up 42 percent of the deaths in this community, with pneumonia, phthis, diarrhea, and diphtheria leading the list of these illnesses (*Annual Report*, 1909; *Annual Report*, 1897).

Students learned that between 1892 and 1893 there was a 30 percent increase in suicide and that immigrants accounted for 80 percent of these suicides. They further examined how the social, economic, and political factors around 1893 may have affected the suicide rates among the immigrant population. The financial depression of 1893 in the United States surely may have contributed to the increase in the number of suicides during this period. Students explored crime statistics, literacy rates, and houses of worship, social services, and other important community support. They could visualize the effects of—or lack of—these supports by the outcomes they observed in the morbidity and mortality rates (*Annual Report*, 1897).

Students also read some of Wald's writings and began to learn about the programs that Wald and Brewster, along with the Henry Street nurses, brought to the community. The Henry Street visiting nurses, the students learned, lived at the settlement house and became neighbors of the families they served. They read about Wald's famous "baptism by fire" where she meets a young child who led her through the streets of the Lower East Side to visit her mother who had been hemorrhaging for 2 days in bed after a difficult childbirth. Wald's graphic description provides a stark reality that students could relate to the experience. Wald wrote (1915):

> Through Hester and Division streets we went to the end of Ludlow; past odorous fish-stands, for the streets were a market-place, unregulated, unsupervised, unclean; past evil-smelling, uncovered garbage-cans; and—perhaps worst of all, where so many little children played. . . . The child led me on through a tenement hallway, across a court where open and unscreened closets were promiscuously used by men and women, up into a rear tenement, by slimy steps whose accumulated dirt was augmented that day by the mud of the streets, and finally into the sickroom. . . . Although the family of seven shared their two rooms with boarders . . . and although

the sick woman lay on a wretched, unclean bed, soiled with a hemorrhage two days old, they were not degraded human beings . . . that morning's experience was a baptism of fire." (pp. 5–6)

Soon after Wald met the family of seven, she and her friend, Mary Brewster, began the Henry Street Settlement for the expressed purpose of improving the unhealthy living conditions they found in the community. Both nurses were social activists and strove to improve the life of the residents of the Lower East Side through political action and nursing interventions. Wald, especially, felt that nurses had the knowledge and skills to advocate political changes to improve the health of the families in the community. Wald (1900/1991) explained that

> among the many opportunities for civic and altruistic work pressing on all sides nurses having superior advantages in their practical training should not rest content with being only nurses, but should use their talents wherever possible in reform and civic movements. (p. 318)

Wald's belief that nurses were poised to advocate for change in the social, economic, and political conditions of the community in which they lived, led to many of the reforms that contributed to the health of the citizens in the community. For example, Wald visited families in their home providing access to nursing care; organized well-baby classes for new mothers; advocated the first school nurse program in New York City which placed a nurse in a city school; established a playground in the community, one of the first of its kind; and fostered an intellectual community of nurses who actively lobbied for social and political changes that supported the health of the citizens in the community.

Given the data that the students collected in their community assessment, they felt that there was synergy between the programs that Wald established and the data they collected. Through the data, they witnessed the sights that Wald and Brewster saw as they made decisions to provide primary health care in the community. Students also saw the similarities between 1893 and the current period of time. What seemed to exist in 1893 continued to exist in a different (but similar) form. Access to care, a rise in tuberculosis, women as primary caregivers, a close relationship between poverty and access to care, large groups of immigrant populations, the need for social and political activism to support health care initiatives, and environmental factors affecting the health of children and adults in the community continue to be concerns in the same community in the twenty-first century. While variations exist today on the particular environmental concerns, patterns of immigration, and political climate, what continues to be a constant is the need for nurses to make decisions about care and provide leadership in improving the health of individuals, families, and the communities they serve.

The graduate students' use of history to learn about community assessments, community action, and nursing's role in political activism helped decide the kinds of health-promoting interventions they could use in their own community clinical experience. Understanding the history of Henry Street offers a way for students to see how decisions were made in the past and to value the remarkable outcomes that these decisions rendered in the nursing profession and the health of the community. They used some of the ideas of the past and introduced them with the ideas that they learned about primary health care in the twenty-first century. Teaching parenting skills, like Wald did in 1893, were one of the projects students initiated at Henry Street's abused women's shelter. Classes in parenting, nutrition, and other health promotion–type activities, which reflected current thinking of the nursing students, continued in the kinds of programming that the original public health nurses of the settlement house offered to the community. Students also saw the leadership displayed by Wald and other public health nurses in the late nineteenth and early twentieth centuries and how their activism continued to be a model for them today.

Nursing History Informs the Decision-Making Process

History provides a knowledge base that allows nurses to better understand their practice and profession. Knowing the evolution of nursing care, or the reasons why nurses for almost 100 years debate the educational level into practice, or why each state requires separate licensing of nursing professionals, affords nurses a way to understand the challenges that the profession has faced over time. Historical understanding allows for thoughtful decisions that facilitate innovation and change. Sometimes, however, tradition is mistaken for historical knowledge and thus, confounds the decision-making process. Pape (2003) states that an organization's valuing of tradition may cause an organization to oppose changes in practice (p. 156). While tradition is part of history, understanding the origins of tradition through historical research allows a basis for comparison, critique, and ultimately decisions that allow for change. Historical research rather than tradition should be the key element used in providing evidence to support decision-making efforts of nursing professionals.

Historical evidence provides depth and context to issues nurses face today and as a result, the American Association for the History of Nursing (AAHN) supports the inclusion of nursing history in the curriculum. Keeling (2001) writes in an AAHN position paper, that "nurses in the 21st century will need more than sheer information; they will need a greater sensitivity to contextual variables and ambiguity if they are to critically evaluate the information they receive" (Keeling, 2001). Nurses need the ability to study, understand, and value history. Integrating nursing history into nursing curricula at all levels is essential to help nurses identify their history; obtain the necessary skills to explore, study, and understand their history; and to ultimately use history in their decision-making process (Lewenson, 2004; Keeling, 2001).

Studying history provides nurses a conceptualization of the modern nursing movement from 1873 to the present day and affords a continuity between the past and present. This continuity allows for nurses to avoid the familiar adage: "Those who do not study history are doomed to repeat it." For nurses, not using history in the decision-making process may waste valuable time and resources in reinventing what was already previously discovered to work (or not work). Not using history also may deny the success of decisions made in nursing education, practice, research, or administration. Nurses need to know what worked and what did not work, and how they can seek the data to support decisions that need to be made by nurses. History is a valuable resource as a knowledge base and allows for its use as a form of evidence. The graduate students in the case study "saw" the conditions the newly immigrated families experienced in 1893 and some of the primary health care needs that Wald and her colleagues at the Henry Street Settlement met. Without understanding the historical significance of the Lower East Side, the graduate students would miss the origins of some of the socially minded programs and ideology of the settlement houses that continue to exist in this area today.

Strumpf and Tomes (1993) examined the historical use of restraints in "troublesome patients" in the United States during the nineteenth century. They observed a difference between the common use of restraints in the United States versus the infrequent use of such devices in Great Britain. The cultural beliefs about the kind of care that these patients, including the mentally ill and the elderly, differed historically in both countries and the outcomes of care varied as well. Strumpf and Tomes recognized the need to study history in order for nurse administrators and nurses to examine their decisions about the use of restraints and to give them a better understanding of why they continue to use them with the elderly when evidence does not support the use of these devices.

> Contemporary observers often assume that this modern restraint crisis is a peculiar product of the late twentieth century, with its large population of aged and chronically ill, fiscal crisis, institutional overcrowding, and staff turnover. . . . Many of the contemporary dilemmas involving physical restraint can be traced back to an earlier "restraint crisis" that occurred during the middle of the nineteenth century. (Strumpf & Tomes, 1993, p. 4)

Like Strumpf and Tomes, historians search for reasons why things occurred and do so in the hope of informing contemporary issues that need thoughtful decisions. When nurses do a nursing assessment on a patient, they start with a nursing history. Nurses would not be able to appropriately assess their patients or develop plans of action without one. If that is the case, why would nursing leaders, educators, practitioners, researchers, and the like attempt to make decisions without getting the history first?

A Historical Look at Decision-Making in Nursing

In exploring the use of nursing history in decision-making, it would be important to look at the history of decision-making in nursing or when and how nurses made decisions. Questions arise such as whether nurses actually made decisions overtly or did they "downplay" their own reasoning abilities to avoid alienating physicians if they assumed a more autonomous role? Did nurses always make decisions about care and about the profession? If so, what kinds of evidence did they use to make these decisions? How did they document these decisions? Were nurses more autonomous in their roles as nurses, such as the ones that Hallett, Abendstern, and Wade (2006) or that Keeling (2006) describe in their work or were nurses merely following physician orders as they cared for their patients? How did nursing's close ties with the women's movement in the late 1800s and early 1900s affect the way nurses made decisions? Were nurses afraid of alienating politicians who could possibly assist the nursing profession obtain nursing registration laws as Lewenson (1993) suggests or did they speak out in favor of women suffrage, regardless of how it affected these politicians? Did Wald and Brewster use the same available demographic data as in the case study about the Lower East Side when determining the need for health care programs in the community? Have nurses historically used "evidence" to support their practice? If so, what kind of evidence did they use and how did they find the evidence?

Nursing research, important to the decision-making process, evolved in the profession as nursing educators and leaders called for nurses to base their clinical decisions on empirical evidence. Nursing educator R. Louise McManus (1961) asked the question: "What is the place of nursing research—yesterday, today, and tomorrow" (p. 76) and examined the evolution of nursing research. She understood the need to look at how research influenced the decisions of nursing leaders in order to plan for the future in nursing. McManus explained that nursing research—or the "methodological search for nursing knowledge"—differed from other professional groups because early studies focused more on nursing education and service rather than on practice.

She reasoned that interest in nursing research differed from other professions because of the different "pressures upon the profession as a whole by social, political, and economic forces and the impact on nursing advances in scientific knowledge" (p. 76).

McManus (1961) highlights the early research efforts of Nightingale, and the later studies of M. Adelaide Nutting, Isabel Stewart, and others who examined nursing education and the status of the profession. The studies, McManus said, usually were implemented by the professional organizations, like the American Society of Superintendents of Training Schools for Nurses (which was renamed the National League of Nursing Education in 1912, and then the National League for Nursing in 1952), and as a result focused more on the issues related to education. Nurse educators, like Stewart, valued research and participated in and led many such endeavors such as her noted time-and-motion studies. Another noted nursing leader, Virginia Henderson, published early scientific studies such as the one McManus includes on "Medical and Surgical Asepsis" in 1939. Structure studies of how the professional organizations should look also were done and dramatically influenced the change in nursing organizations in the early 1950s.

McManus's (1961) examination of history provides a view of the development of nursing research prior to the early 1960s that explains as well as raises questions about nursing's interest in research and the subsequent culture of research. She noted that the way nursing organized around issues of practice and service as well as one of the first graduate educational programs for nurses situated in Teachers College, Columbia University (a college for teachers), was indicative of the kinds of studies and research of early nursing. McManus (1961) wrote that: "This happenstance of teachers pushing toward education and toward a teacher training institution for the first graduate programs may well have affected the course of nursing's development considerably" (p. 79).

Many in nursing were interested in knowledge building to support decisions in nursing. In her 1934 article in the *American Journal of Nursing*, Sister M. Bernice Beck called for nurses to base their practice on scientific principles rather than on outdated models that supported a paternalistic hierarchy. Nurses, especially educators and administrators, needed to have a "scientific attitude," which Beck described as being

> . . . openminded, ready to learn the truth and accept it; observant, keen, clear-minded, cautious, alert, vigorous, original, and independent in thinking; she carefully weighs all the evidence and overlooks no factor which may influence the results; allows no personal preferences to influence decisions; holds only tentative scientific convictions, because aware that we have not yet arrived at the end of knowledge, but are constantly wresting more secrets from the hidden depths of Nature." (p. 580)

The early move toward basing practice on nursing research required that nurses examine the way they carried out procedures and not just accept what they did without first examining the outcomes of their actions. Beck wrote that the teacher of nursing arts

> never insists that procedures, as taught, are the last word; that the unfounded statements of textbooks must be accepted without question, and that the ordering physician must be looked upon as an infallible authority. On the contrary, she urges her students to find out why things are done as they are; whether there are not better ways of doing them; to challenge statements, to ask for proofs, to think for themselves, to make individual contributions. (p. 581)

Students were expected to learn to question and to make decisions based on the response to their questions. Decisions were not to be made by rote; rather they needed to be made using research data. Harmer and Henderson (1940) in their noted text, *The Principles and Practice of Nursing*, included a section on the "Professional Responsibilities in Relation to Method." Nurses were to "accept the responsibility for studying its procedures and designing its method" (p. 469).

In order to understand how decisions in nursing are made and the kinds of decision-making models or frameworks available, it is important to remember to place decisions within a context that looks at the particular period in which those decisions are made. The students in the case study presented earlier in this chapter examined the demographic data and the morbidity and mortality rates of the Lower East Side within the context of the late nineteenth-century United States. They explored the meaning of immigration within the social, political, and economic period of the day. In this way, they could compare and contrast the health care decisions that were made by nurses during that period with the more contemporary decisions made today in the same community. This may be beyond the scope of this chapter, but it is something to consider when looking at history and decision-making in nursing.

Historical Critiques Assist Decision-Making in Nursing

Historiography provides the data and the necessary critique that nurses require in their decision-making process. Lewenson (2007) shows how studies in nursing education, practice, and administration provide historical evidence that nurses may use when making decisions on such issues as appropriate educational levels in nursing, the role of the nurse practitioner, and resolving the nursing shortage. Studies like the one that Whelan (2005) did on exploring the demise of private duty nursing in the United States provides data for a discussion about nursing shortage, staffing issues, and changes in the hospital settings. R. A. Seeger Jablonski's (2003) study examines the history of the nurse practitioner movement and the effect on nursing education at the Virginia Commonwealth University (VCU). The historical account at VCU serves as a way of knowing what happened to this particular program and serves as an example of how other programs may have fared during the same time period.

Historical studies provide explanations, connections, and relationships among variables in the past and can be used to assist today's nurses in the decision-making process. For example, understanding the history of nursing's clinical practice provides knowledge of what worked in the past and perhaps how it can improve. Historical studies, such as Keeling's (2006) "Medicines in the Work of Henry Street Settlement Visiting Nurses," explores the role the settlement nurses played in giving medications and nursing interventions, thus, illuminating questions about the work of visiting nurses, autonomy, prescriptive privileges, and legal boundaries of practice today. These visiting nurses in the late nineteenth and early twentieth century gave medications that were sometimes prescribed, as well as gave medications that were not. These nurses sought the over-the-counter treatments that both nurses and laypeople often used to heal a wound or cure a cold.

Keeling describes how these treatments fell somewhere in the middle, using Lavinia Dock's (author of the 1898 *Materia Medica for Nurses*) term describing the role of the nurse as being in the "middle place" or somewhere between "professional medical service and unskilled family caregiving"(2006, p. 9). Keeling also noted that nurses did not write about their administration of medications, frequently taking this part of their work for granted as well as trying to minimize it. The research showed how the Henry Street Settlement House (HSS) visiting nurses challenged the boundaries of the early nurse practice acts and sought to provide access to care, often diagnosing, prescribing, and carrying out treatments, without the direct supervision as was required by law of the physician.

Why Keeling's 2006 research is important to decision-making is found in any number of contemporary discussions addressing the role of nurses, autonomy of practice, nurse practitioner licensure, the move toward a doctor of nursing practice, changes in licensure for health care professionals, and other issues affecting nursing education, practice, and research. Keeling uncovers how little is known of the work of the HSS visiting nurses. This group of professionals often has been studied from a social-political perspective about their activities and the effect they had on improving the environment for the families and individuals they served in the Lower East Side community in New York City rather than on their actual clinical practice.

Nurses today who work with families in the home may also struggle with dispensing advice about medications and offering information about health care interventions typically found in the home. Families today have greater access and knowledge about these medications, but may be hampered by restrictions set by nurse practice acts that prohibit nurses prescribing medications. Given the greater access to the Internet, television, newspapers, or magazines, consumer levels of understanding have been raised and with that their expectations about care.

This "middle place" that Dock describes in her 1898 book and Keeling refers to in her 2006 article is specifically directed toward nurses. Dock wrote her book for nurses to learn about drugs and their administration from the standpoint of what nurses needed to know rather than from what physicians needed to know. Until 1890, when Dock first published her book, the medical perspective was the only one available. Nurses learned about pharmacology from the books available at the time, and not until Dock wrote hers specifically for nurses was the nursing intervention and role of the nurse addressed.

Another historical study by Hallett, Abendstern, and Wade (2006) examines the autonomous clinical practice of the industrial nurse in England around the mid-twentieth century. In the cotton factories, concern for the health of the workers, mostly women, was in the hands of the "welfare officer." The welfare officer usually had formal nurse's training or in some instances they were not nurses, but had first-aid training. Hallett, Abendstern, and Wade conclude that little is known about the clinical side of industrial nursing and the history of this specialty has been overlooked in general by nursing. Hallett, Abendstern, and Wade used oral histories of cotton factory workers as well as three of the welfare officers to gain insight into the autonomous nature of this role and how it shaped the care of a group of cotton workers in the middle of the twentieth century. The outcome of the study describes the values that these particular nurses ascribed to in the fulfillment of their responsibilities. The welfare officers who were nurses worked autonomously providing nursing interventions, that like Keeling's study, revealed they dispensed medications and nursing treatments that relied on their own nursing assessment and diagnosis. Hallett, Abendstern, and Wade (2006) stated that these nurses were imbued "with a sense of autonomy and a consciousness of the 'expert' nature of their role. They were not willing to be 'told their job' by mill owners" (p. 103). The interventions were mostly first aid in nature and did not seem to cover preventative, screening-type interventions that would have promoted health care of employees. The written record is more limited and the history of this period is captured mostly through oral history, without which, the knowledge would no longer be accessible (Hallett, Abendstern, & Wade, 2006, p. 103).

Both Keeling (2006) and Hallett, Abendstern, and Wade (2006) provide today's nurses with data of what was done in the past. They uncover the history of working nurses and make connections between then and now. Keeler, for example, links the work of the Henry Street nurses in the early twentieth century and the role of nurse practitioners today. Contemporary nurses struggle with decisions about advanced practice, nurse practice acts, and collaborating partnerships with physicians that would all benefit in the knowledge that these two historiographies presented. Uncovering of the history informs not only the practice, but the education and research as well and thus affects nursing outcomes today and in the future. Today's professionals can learn from the wisdom, knowledge, mistakes, and vision of those earlier nurses.

Another Case Study

In 1996 when I was an instructor in a community health course on the Lower East Side in New York City, one of the students, who was a registered nurse returning to school for a baccalaureate degree in nursing, was visiting a "client" of the Henry Street Settlement Home Health Care agency in the home. The student professionally worked as a cardiac care nurse and was proficient in providing high-level care using the latest technology in cardiac care. However, when she entered this client's home during the community clinical rotation, she said she was shocked at the odor emanating from the client's feet and had difficulty knowing what her responsibilities were in this case. She wanted to know what could be done for this client, because there were no medical orders and she felt she could not do anything without them.

The goal of the community experience at the Henry Street Settlement (where the visiting nursing service had separated from the agency in 1944) was to visit clients who received homemaking services in the home. Students were expected to develop a nursing plan of care after completing a nursing assessment of the client, the client's concerns, the homemaker's concern, and an assessment of the home and community resources. When I visited the client's home with the student nurse and saw the caked-on dirt and smelled the odor from the feet, I asked the homemaker to prepare a basin of warm water so that we could soak the client's feet. We instituted a nursing intervention, bathing of the feet, so that we could further assess the skin color, the temperature, and the integrity of the skin. As we bathed the feet, the student spoke with the client and began to build trust with him and develop a rapport with the homemaker. Following the simple "nursing" procedure, the student patted the feet dry, continued to assess the feet, and began to teach the client about proper foot care.

The student said on the walk back to Henry Street that while she could operate efficiently in the hospital setting, the home-care setting created new challenges to her perceived role of the nurse. She was unaware of what visiting nurses did or had done in the past. She lacked historical perspective that might have assisted her in understanding this middle ground where nurses provide nursing care autonomously. The autonomous role that she was learning in the community clinical experience had ties with earlier nurses in the same community. Yet not knowing the past creates challenges for her and all nurses who make decisions in their practice.

Conclusion

History provides today's nurses with an "overarching conceptual framework that allows us to more fully understand the disparate meaning of nursing and the different experiences of nurses" (D'Antonio, 2003, p. 1). Lynaugh and Reverby (1987) said that history "provides us with the tools to examine the full range of human existence and to assess the constraints under which decisions are made" (Lynaugh & Reverby, 1987, p. 4). Without understanding nursing history, decisions are at risk of failing and repeating past errors. Historiography provides a way of knowing and understanding of what has gone on before, what is happening now, and what may be expected in the future. If all knowledge has a historical dimension, then nurses need to take this dimension into account whenever a decision is made. All decisions, regardless of the decision-making approach that nurses may use, also must include an historical dimension in the matrix. Like the case studies presented and the historiographies identified, nurses can learn from understanding the past and using this understanding to support the kinds of decisions that they make today.

> History is alive, and the search for answers in history is useful for solving present difficulties, directing behavior, and accomplishing the objectives of the nursing profession. When the answers are found, it is not the end. It is the beginning (Austin, 1978, p. viii).

References

Annual Report of the Board of Health of the Department of Health of the City of New York VII, 1908. (1909). New York: Martin, Printers, & Stationers.

Annual Report of the Board of Health of the Health Department of the City of New York for the year ending December 31, 1893. (1897). New York: Martin B. Brown, Printers and Stationers.

Austin, A. L. (1978). Foreword. In M. Louise Fitzpatrick, ed. *Historical studies in nursing: Papers presented at the 15th Annual Stewart Conference on Research in Nursing March 1977*, pp. vii–viii. New York: Teachers College Press.

Beck, M. B. (1934). Coordinating the teaching of sciences and nursing practice: Underlying scientific principles in nursing practice. *The American Journal of Nursing, 34(6)*, pp. 579–586. Located through JSTOR Wednesday, January 17, 2007 at 10:46:38.

Christy, T. E. (1978). The hope of history. In M. Louise Fitzpatrick, Ed. *Historical studies in nursing: Papers presented at the 15th Annual Stewart Conference on Research in Nursing March 1977* (pp. 3–11). New York: Teachers College Press.

D'Antonio, P. (2003). Editor's note. *Nursing History Review, 11*, p. 1.

Dock, L. L. (1898). *Text-book of materia medica for nurses* (3rd ed. rev. and enlarged). New York: G. P. Putnam's Sons.

Hallett, C., Abendstern, M., & Wade, L. (2006). Industry and autonomy in early occupational health nursing: The welfare officers of the Lancashire cotton mills in the mid-twentieth century. *Nursing History Review, 14*, pp. 89–109.

Harmer, B., & Henderson, V. (1940). *Textbook of the principles and practice of nursing* (4th ed., revised). New York: MacMillan Company.

Keeling, A. (2001). *Nursing history in the curriculum: Preparing nurses for the 21st century*. AAHN position paper. Retrieved August 8, 2006, from http://aahn.org/position.html

Keeling, A. (2006). Medicines in the work of Henry Street Settlement Visiting Nurses. *Nursing History Review, 14*, pp. 7–30. New York: Springer.

Lewenson, S. B. (1993). *Taking charge: Nursing, suffrage, and feminism in America, 1873–1920*. New York: Garland.

Lewenson, S. B. (2004). Integrating nursing history into the curriculum. *Journal of Professional Nursing, 20(6)*, 347–380.

Lewenson, S. B. (2007). Chapter 12: Historical research in practice, education, and administration. In H. J. Speziale & D. R. Carpenter (Eds.). *Qualitative research in nursing: Advancing the humanistic imperative*, 4th ed. (pp. 273–300). Philadelphia: Lippincott.

Lynaugh, J., & Reverby, S. (1987). Thoughts on the nature of history. *Nursing Research, 36(1)*, 4, 69.

McManus, R. L. (1961). Nursing research—Its evolution. *American Journal of Nursing, 61(4)*, pp. 76–79. Retrieved February 26, 2007, from http://links.jstor.org/sici?sici=0002-936X%28196104%2961%3A4%3C76%3ANRIE%3E2.0.CO%3B2-P

Nelson, S., & Gordon, S. (2004). The rhetoric of rupture: Nursing as practice with a history? *Nursing Outlook, 52*, 255–261.

Pape, T. M. (2003). Evidence-based nursing practice: To infinity and beyond. *Journal of Continuing Education in Nursing, 34(4)*, 154–161.

Roberts, M. (1939). Current events and trends in nursing. *American Journal of Nursing, 39(1)*, 1–8. Retrieved January 17, 2007, from http://links.jstor.org/sici?sici=0002-936X%28193901%2939%3A1%3C1%3ACEATIN%3E2.0.CO%3B2-U

Seeger Jablonski, R. A. (2003). Sparks to wildfires: The emergence and impact of nurse practitioner education at Virginia Commonwealth University 1974–1991. *Nursing History Review, 11,* 167–185. New York: Springer Publishing Company.

Strumpf, N. E., & Tomes, N. (1993). Restraining the troublesome patient: A historical perspective on a contemporary debate. *Nursing History Review, 1,* 1–24.

Wald, L. D. (1900). Work of women in municipal affairs. *Proceedings of the Sixth Annual Convention of the American Society of Superintendents of Nurses* (pp. 54–57). Harrisburg, PA: Harrisburg Pub. Reprinted in Birnbach, N., & Lewenson, S. B. (Eds.) (1991). *First words: Selected addresses from the National League for Nursing, 1894–1933* (pp. 315–318). New York: NLN.

Wald, L. D. (1915). *The house on Henry Street.* New York: Henry Holt and Company.

Whelan, J. (2005). 'A necessity in the nursing world': The Chicago Nurses Professional Registry, 1913–1950. *Nursing History Review, 13,* 49–75.

Media and Decision-Making

Sandy Summers, MSN, MPH, RN
and Harry Jacobs Summers, JD

> **Four hostile newspapers are more to be feared
> than a thousand bayonets.**
> —Napoleon Bonaparte (1769–1821)

The modern media is pervasive and highly influential. It shapes our culture, our government, and our lives. English statesman Edmund Burke (1739–1797) termed the media the "fourth estate," when he proclaimed its strength greater than all the "three estates in Parliament" (Newspaper Association, 2005). Thousands of times every day, the media presents society with a persuasive vision of what society is, what it might be, and what it should be. The media investigates, hosts, and fosters public dialogue, and it regularly influences public decision-making, operating largely outside the domain of government officials in free societies.

The media does more than a government body. The media influences and even creates much of our culture. Its power lies in changing the way people think. U.S. advertisers spend $500 billion per year to buy media (Young, 2006). Those who spend these vast sums clearly believe that people will take actions based on advertising's persuasive, one-sided flows of information on subjects where viewers/readers may not have a great deal of prior experience or knowledge. This is also why powerful political ads can move polling numbers and affect election results. In addition, research shows that the news and entertainment media affect what people believe and how they act on a wide range of issues, including health-related issues.

Clearly, the media also has a tremendous impact on how the public sees health care, including nurses and nursing practice. At every moment of every day, the media sends the public powerful messages, not only about important issues like cancer or health insurance, but about who nurses are, what they know, what they do, and how much their work matters. These messages drive decision-making in all areas and at all levels, including the actions of patients, nurses and their colleagues, hospital managers, top federal officials and the voters who elect them. The media thus plays a critical role in shaping the current state of nursing care, and, particularly because the media's overall treatment of nursing is deeply flawed and damaging, it offers important avenues for nurses to improve their situation and the care of their patients.

This chapter starts with a case study that illustrates the media's effect on the population, the image of nurses in the media, and the work that nurses need to do to change that image so that they gain a respected place in health care decision-making. This chapter then presents a discussion about how nurses can use the media to increase their visibility, improve their image, and thus become valued decision-makers in health care.

Case Study

In November 2001, as part of the "Closing the Health Gap" campaign of the U.S. Department of Health and Human Services (HHS), the HHS Office of Minority Health (OMH) launched a new health initiative: the "Take a Loved One to the Doctor Day" campaign ("Loved One" campaign). The "Loved One" campaign was cofounded by HHS and ABC Radio's Urban Advantage Network, which has a weekly reach of more than 19 million listeners (HHS Press Office, 2004). The "Loved One" campaign's goal was to encourage members of minority populations to take charge of their personal health by educating and empowering them. The campaign would be held each year on the third Tuesday of September.

The "Loved One" campaign soon came to the attention of a small group of graduate students at the Johns Hopkins University School of Nursing. These students had just formed a group called the Nursing Vision. The purpose of the Nursing Vision was to increase public understanding of nursing and improve media images of nursing, which seemed especially urgent in view of the global nursing shortage. The group was concerned that the U.S. government would be promoting this worthy public health campaign with a name that excluded the work of the advanced practice registered nurses (APRNs) who provide a great deal of primary care to the underserved populations the campaign targets.

The "Loved One" issue came to the attention of the Nursing Vision and group members decided to take action. Several members sent letters and made telephone calls to the general number at OMH in early 2002, asking that the Office consider changing the campaign name to one that did not exclude APRNs.

When Sandy Summers, the Nursing Vision's cofounder, made a call to OMH, she was told that the office would never change the name of the campaign, because the word "doctor" tested so well in focus groups. After a time, the Nursing Vision set the matter aside, concluding that HHS was unlikely to change the name.

Later in 2002, Summers began to work full time on creating a more formal organization to address the widespread misunderstanding of nursing. The group incorporated, applied to the Internal Revenue Service for 501(c)(3) nonprofit status, and changed its name to the Center for Nursing Advocacy. Summers became the group's executive director. In late 2002, the Center launched a Web site, www.nursingadvocacy.org, on which it started analyzing nursing depictions in the media. The Center also began sending news alerts to supporters and encouraged them to send letters to the media to ask for more accurate depictions of nursing.

Soon, the Center began having some success in convincing corporations to end or modify advertising that used stereotypical images of nurses. A late 2003 Washington Post story covered the Center's campaign to convince the television show ER to depict nurses more accurately, and that story traveled across the globe (Center for Nursing Advocacy, 2003b). With experience and the increase in membership, the Center was becoming more effective.

In October 2004, the Center received a call from the American College of Nurse-Midwives (ACNM). ACNM remained concerned that the "Loved One" campaign name reinforced the damaging idea that only physicians provide primary care. The Center decided to renew its efforts to persuade OMH to change the name. The Center was now much larger, it had a powerful tool at its disposal—the web page from which a form e-mail letter could be sent. That tool had been essential to many of the Center's other successes.

Summers gathered information. She did research on the Internet and through calls to OMH collected the names and contact information of high-ranking individuals who would be involved in any decision to rename the campaign. This was a critical advocacy step—find the real decision-makers—and one that had not been employed in the Nursing Vision's 2002 efforts.

Summers also collected research comparing the care provided by physicians to the care provided by APRNs. The Center built a web page featuring the studies she found comparing the care of the two groups. The consensus of this research was that care provided by APRNs was as good as or better than that provided by physicians. This research would help to show why the "Loved One" campaign had no reason to exclude APRNs.

In the meantime, the ACNM drafted a proposed letter to OMH, which it sent to the Center for review in November 2004. In the letter, ACNM suggested five possible new names for the "Loved One" campaign, one of which was "Take a Loved One for a Checkup Day." The Center then drafted an analysis of the issue, which explained why the current name of the campaign was so damaging.

With the analysis ready, the Center prepared a letter to be sent to OMH. The Center embraced the ACNM's suggested name change of "Take a Loved One for a Checkup Day." On December 7, 2004, Summers e-mailed the letter to the Assistant Secretary for Minority Health and about seven other people at OMH, as well as the Secretary of HHS, and the host of a popular, nationally syndicated urban radio show, who had been the honorary chair of the "Loved One" campaign since its inception. Around this same time, ACNM and the American Academy of Nurse Practitioners (AANP) sent their own letters and urged their members to support the Center's campaign to have the name changed; a number of these members visited the Center's web site and sent letters using the site.

The Center also included a "Take Action" item on the "Loved One" campaign in its news alert of December 7. The item asked people to write to OMH and the other decision-makers. To make that easier, the item included a link to a proposed e-mail letter that had been adapted from the Center's letter to the decision-makers. Supporters were able to simply sign this form letter, or draft their own letter, then send the result to the decision-makers. On December 17, the Center issued a press release, but the media failed to pick up the story.

Letters from the Center's web site began rolling in to HHS from concerned nurses and supporters. The letters appeared to be reaching the e-mail inboxes of at least some of the decision-makers.

In mid-December 2004, Summers called OMH and asked to set up a telephone call with the Assistant Secretary for Minority Health, an executive who was relatively new to the job and had not been with

OMH in 2002. By this time, OMH had received about 200 letters from the Center's web site. After a number of requests, the call was arranged.

On December 21, Summers had a conference call with the Assistant Secretary and another OMH decision-maker. During the call, Summers explained the problem with the "Doctor Day" part of the campaign name and stressed how helpful a change would be. The Assistant Secretary was receptive, and he agreed to explore the idea of a name change. The Center kept the campaign open, and on January 3, 2005, Summers sent the Assistant Secretary an e-mail requesting more definitive action on OMH plans to change the "Doctor Day" name so the Center could end its campaign. Around this time, OMH staff members assured Summers that a letter from the Assistant Secretary would be forthcoming.

On January 12, 2005, American Nurses Association president Barbara Blakeney sent the HHS decision-makers a letter about the name change that was drawn largely from the center's model.

On January 28, 2005, the Assistant Secretary for Minority Health sent the Center and the other nursing groups a letter confirming that HHS working groups would seek a new name for the campaign. The Center ended its active campaign about the name. At this point, OMH had received about 370 letters from the Center's web site.

In July 2005, OMH began issuing materials relating to the upcoming September campaign day. These materials showed that OMH had changed the name to "Take a Loved One for a Checkup Day," as the Center and ACNM had suggested. The OMH campaign used that name in 2005 and 2006, and almost all of the campaign's media and health care partners used the new name as well. Unfortunately, the host of the popular syndicated show on ABC Radio's Urban Advantage Network, who continued to serve as honorary co-chair of the campaign, refused to use the new name. His office dismissed the Center's concerns, telling Summers in a phone call that the change could have "harmful effects" and that the original name had "capital." Thus, working for universal buy-in of the "Checkup Day" name continues to be an important goal for the Center going forward. (See **Figure   1**.)

This case study is an example of how one small group decided to take action and place constructive pressure on a very powerful second group. This pressure, applied via the use of media strategies, caused a shift in the second group's perceptions, resulting in a decision to change the name of a prominent national media campaign. The tactics used may be applied in any venue where the message of the media would help effect positive change. The change in the title of this media campaign gave the public greater awareness of and thus access to health care providers other than the "doctor," and it potentially improved understanding of the value of nurses and their ability to be included as decision-makers in health care.

Source: U.S. Department of Health and Human Services.

The Pervasive Influence of the Media

The average American spends 3,518 hours per year, or 60 percent of that person's awake time, consuming media (U.S. Census Bureau, 2007). Research shows that this media—including advertising and entertainment programming—has a significant impact on what consumers think and do. Nurses therefore have an enormous opportunity to bring messages about nursing and health care generally to patients and society at large by tapping into the insatiable desire for media entertainment and information. Unfortunately, although there have been accurate and helpful depictions of nursing, too much of the media's depiction of the profession has been damaging. This poor depiction affects the public's ideas about the value of nursing, and about nurses' role and influence in health care decision-making.

Effects of Media on Health Care and Nursing

In recent years, a consensus has emerged in the field of public health, based on considerable research, that what people see in the media has a significant effect on their health-related views and behavior. A wide range of public agencies, private groups, and scholars now devote substantial resources to analyzing and managing health messages in the media. This is part of the public health field called *health communications.*

Health communications is a "hybrid" with roots in communications, health care, and other fields (Glik, 2003). Glik (2003) states that health communications contain both planned and unplanned messages that can be positive, neutral, or negative. These unplanned messages are significant in that people are influenced by media content whether or not the creators specifically intended that they take away the message received.

What the media tells people about health care works much like advertising. As one public health scholar noted "[f]rom a social marketing perspective, messages in the media that promote specific desirable behaviors have the potential to persuade consumers to change their behavior if messages are viewed as compatible with consumers' own self-interest, competing messages are minimal, and resistance to change is low to moderate" (Glik, 2003, p. 1).

News media coverage also affects the public's perception and beliefs about health care (Turow & Gans, 2002). Because treatment of health topics in the news media has a significant effect on public views and actions, advocates have worked hard to affect the frequency and accuracy of the media's coverage of health topics in which they have an interest (Glik, 2003).

Media influence is hardly confined to hard-news outlets. On the contrary, what people see in the fictional media has a significant effect on their health-related views and behavior as well. In 2000, the U.S. Centers for Disease Control and Prevention surveyed prime-time TV viewers and found that most (52%) reported getting information that they trust to be accurate from prime-time TV shows (Henry J. Kaiser Family Foundation, 2004). More than a quarter of this survey's respondents said such shows were among their top three sources for health information (Henry J. Kaiser, 2004). Nine out of 10 regular viewers said they learned something about diseases or disease prevention from television, with almost half citing prime-time or daytime entertainment shows (Henry J. Kaiser, 2004). Moreover, almost half of regular viewers who heard something about a health issue on a prime-time show said they took one or more actions, including telling someone about the storyline (42%), telling someone to do something (such as using a condom or getting more exercise) or doing it themselves (16%), or visiting a clinic (9%) (Henry J. Kaiser, 2004).

Some research has focused on the effects of specific shows, particularly the popular NBC drama ER. This show has been on the air since 1994 and is now shown in many nations around the world. During the U.S. television seasons running during 1997–2000, the Henry J. Kaiser Family Foundation surveyed 3,500 regular ER viewers (Brodie et al., 2001; Henry J. Kaiser, 2003; Henry J. Kaiser, 2002). In the Kaiser surveys, more than half (53%) of regular ER viewers said they learned about important health issues while watching the show. Almost a third said information from the show helped them make choices about their own family's health care; this was especially true of viewers with less-formal education (44% with no college versus 25% with some college). As a result of watching ER, almost a quarter of viewers said they sought further information about a health issue, and 14 percent actually contacted a health care provider because of something they saw in an ER episode.

At least one study suggested a link between public attitudes toward nursing and ER. In a 2000 JWT Communications focus group study of youngsters in grades 2–10, respondents said they received their main impression of nursing from ER (JWT Communications, 2000). Consistent with the show's physician-centric approach, the young people also wrongly believed that nursing was a girl's job, that it was a technical job "like shop," and that it was an inappropriate career for private school students, of whom more was expected (JWT Communications, 2000).

Nursing's Role in Shaping Health Messages

Nurses can help to shape health messages for public consumption. However, the profession's public image may actually impede nurses' efforts to play this role.

Although nurses commonly top polls measuring which professions are the most trusted, any serious evaluation of the profession's public image reveals that most people do not understand what nurses actually do or why nursing work matters (Center for Nursing Advocacy, 2006a). On the contrary, nursing's public image has long been based primarily on stereotypes, including the physician's handmaiden, the angel, and the "naughty nurse" (Center, 2007b; Center, 2007c; Darbyshire & Gordon, 2005; Kalisch & Kalisch, 1986). Thus, while nurses have tended to enjoy public affection, they have not received the real respect that might lead to a better allocation of clinical, educational, and research resources for the profession or allow nurses a real seat at the table of policy-making and clinical decision-making. Nurses' image as workers without significant knowledge also has negatively impacted the public's perception of the validity of information that nurses offer them for health decision-making, both on an individual basis and in wider public forums. To take just one example, consider the primitive depictions of family presence on television dramas, which regularly feature physicians ordering family members far away from patient bedsides during emergency procedures as a matter of course, as if no one had ever questioned this practice. If nurses had meaningful input, it seems likely that such influential shows would be giving the public a better sense of evolving health practices in this regard (Center, 2006g).

Since research shows that the media has such a strong influence on public understanding of nursing and health care in general, it is vital to nursing and public health that nurses improve their media image. Indeed, if the mass media is critical to modern health strategies overall, then it must also be a key means of addressing one of the most important worldwide health problems: the nursing shortage.

Media Portrayal of Nurses: The Stereotypes

The media frequently portrays nursing work because nursing involves life, death, conflict and drama—the stuff of compelling and important media. Unfortunately, the media commonly portrays nurses stereotypically, often crediting physicians for their work, and this is especially true of the most influential media, television. Factors contributing to this may include entrenched social biases (including gender bias) and assumptions about nursing, including:

- The view that smart, ambitious women with an interest in health care necessarily become physicians
- What one scholar has called nursism, a more general social bias against the caring role that contributes negatively to the way nursing is perceived (Lewenson, 1993)
- The media's common reliance on well-understood (but often incorrect) conventions
- A lack of significant support for nursing from the physicians who continue to exercise great influence over the media and who enjoy unparalleled esteem, including the widespread assumption that they provide all important health care
- Nursing's own failure to adequately represent itself to the media and the public at large (Buresh & Gordon, 2006)

There have been notable exceptions, particularly in the print media, in documentaries, and a few fictional products (Center, 2006b). However, the overall impression of nursing the public gets from the media is distorted and inadequate to the needs of nurses and their patients.

The most common nursing stereotypes are:

- **The Physician Handmaiden.** Nurses have long been portrayed as fungible females who have no great level of training, no unique scope of practice, and no significant role in substantive health care. Instead, they are seen to exist to help the physicians who do provide important health care; it is assumed that physicians supervise and manage nurses and know everything

107

nurses do. This is perhaps the most damaging stereotype, because it remains so common and so persuasive to a public that knows little of what nurses really do. Indeed, the hand-maiden remains the central nursing image in popular Hollywood television shows, where the few nurses who appear seem to exist to get physicians or get things for physicians. Handmaiden images range from the less-obviously damaging portrayals of nurses as skilled physician subordinates, as seen on shows like ER and Scrubs, to the explicit attacks on the profession in products like Grey's Anatomy or House, where nurses tend to be clueless, often disagreeable servants who represent everything ambitious modern women have left behind (Center, 2006c).

The "Naughty Nurse." The "naughty nurse" image commonly takes the form of a female model or actress dressed in a supposed "nursing uniform" that amounts to lingerie. Such images remain a staple of media communications of the advertising, apparel, hospitality, and entertainment industries, particularly in products directed at younger males. Some entertainment programming continues to suggest that nurses tend to be sexually available to physicians, one example being the depiction of "skanky syph[ilis] nurse" Olivia on Grey's Anatomy. The Center for Nursing Advocacy (discussed in the earlier case study) has convinced many corporate advertisers to reconsider such images, though the images continue to appear in prominent media worldwide. As the Center explained, even though these images are often "jokes" or "fantasies," the stereotypes they promote discourage practicing and potential nurses, encourage sexual violence in the workplace, and contribute to a general atmosphere of disrespect that make it difficult for nurses to get the respect and resources they need (Center, 2006d).

The Angel. On the surface, the image of nurses as angels is seemingly the best of the stereotypes, and some nurses themselves endorse it. Indeed, the angel image is fueled by some media products that are designed to appeal to nurses, such as uniforms. However, the image of nurses as devoted hand-holders and scut-work saints undervalues nurses' knowledge and advanced skills. It may also allow decision-makers to discount poor working conditions that nurses endure or to treat the conditions as evidence of nurses' virtue, rather than problems that must be addressed. Some nurses, including the Center for Nursing Advocacy, view the Johnson & Johnson (J&J) Campaign for Nursing's Future television commercials as employing this stereotype. These nurses note that a trusted, baby-soft image is obviously helpful to a major pharmaceutical corporation, which benefits by aligning itself with a profession at the pinnacle of public trust, but that nursing itself is not well-served by the perpetuation of the view that nurses are relatively unskilled spiritual beings with no earthly needs (Center, 2006I).

The Battleaxe. The "battleaxe" image essentially presents the nurse as an unattractive, bitter, and malevolent force, often the representation of an unfeeling bureaucracy or institutional oppression. This image continues to appear from time to time in advertising and entertainment programming. The image may stem in part from a need to compensate for a feeling that female nurses may have significant power over vulnerable men in clinical settings, and from a belief that any assertive nurse who fails to conform to the more submissive nursing stereotypes must be a she-demon. Nurse Ratched from *One Flew Over the Cuckoo's Nest* is perhaps the best-known example of the battleaxe, a portrayal that may be the most influential modern image of a nurse who seems to delight in torturing patients. The book and film are assigned to college students across the land, and these artistic and culturally significant works are likely to help perpetuate the battleaxe image for decades to come (Center for Nursing Advocacy, 2003a).

The Physician Golddigger or "Wannabe Mrs. Kovac." This image has long existed in tandem with the strand of the "naughty nurse" image that presents the nurse as being sexually available to physicians. Recent examples include remarks by television psychologist "Dr. Phil" McGraw in 2004, who suggested on the air that the health care system is full of "cute little nurses" who are out to "seduce and marry" physicians "because that's their ticket out of having to work as a nurse." Dr. Phil later made on-air statements expressing support for nursing after the center contacted the show and the show received more than 1,400 letters sent through the Center's Web site (Center for Nursing Advocacy, 2004b).

The Female Caregiver. Even a casual look at the preceding images shows that the most common nursing stereotypes are closely linked to the prevailing assumption that nurses are female caregivers. In the JWT Communications (2000) research of 1,800 U.S. school children in grades 2–10, researchers found that when the focus groups' topic changed to nursing, the boys stopped paying attention, as if the conversation no longer pertained to them. It has been persuasively argued that caregiving has long been admired, but rarely considered intellectually challenging or truly essential outside of the family structure (Nelson & Gordon, 2006). Although there has been recent media about men in nursing and a few minor nurse characters in recent Hollywood shows have been male, major depictions of nurses remain overwhelmingly female. Of course, nursing does remain less than 10 percent male (U.S. Department of Health and Human Services, 2000). However, as long as it is portrayed as a profession that is for "*caring*" *females*, it will be considered work that is too effeminate and insubstantial for men—and too lowly for anyone interested in an autonomous, challenging career.

Any Helpful Person or Thing Is a Nurse. The media, notably in promoting recent feature films like *The Skeleton Key* (2005), has tended to suggest that nursing is something any caring person can do—that any caregiver is a "nurse." Consider the recent growth in "baby nurses," who are actually nannies for newborns who may have no health care training at all. Still, these workers commonly refer to themselves—and are referred to in the major media—by the shorthand "nurse." After one "baby nurse" allegedly injured a newborn in New York in 2005, the state legislature passed a law to prevent nonnurses from calling themselves "nurses" (Center, 2005a). In 2006, the CVS pharmaceutical chain featured a television commercial in which a pharmacist suggested that by helping a patient's spouse learn about her complex medication regimen in half a day, he had turned the spouse into a nurse. After a few calls from the center, CVS removed this statement from its commercial (Center, 2006h). Another common version of this image appears when makers of electronic health care tools that perform relatively simple tasks market their products with names like "electronic nurse," or otherwise suggest that the product will be acting as a nurse, as has been the case with some surgical robots. The media is often eager to call such machines "nurses" (Center, 2006l). The Center has convinced a number of these creators to cease naming their products after skilled nurses.

The Wallpaper Nurse. Nurse characters populate the background of popular television shows like *House* doing busy work as a kind of garnish to the glamorous, important work of the heroic physicians on which the camera focuses. These "wallpaper nurses" may morph out of the background to push gurneys, deliver messages, or hand things to physicians. They often are presented as mute automatons who would seem not to need significant education or resources; certainly few viewers would want to see themselves in such a role. Ironically, the actors playing these roles are often real nurses.

The Physician Nurse. Physician characters on fictional television shows are often presented performing the work that real-life nurses do. There are about 30 major characters on the four top U.S. hospital shows (*Grey's Anatomy, House, ER,* and *Scrubs*). All but two of these characters are physicians. Because the majority of real hospital work is done by nurses, including tasks involving patient interactions and many of the key tasks in critical procedures, the media's physician characters must do nursing jobs just to make the shows' drama work. This effectively gives physicians credit for the exciting work that nurses really do. At the same time, the news media commonly consults only physicians for advice in areas where nurses generally have greater expertise, such as breastfeeding, pain management, and patient education.

The Cut-Rate Physician Substitute. A large body of research shows that the care of APRNs is *at least* as good as that provided by physicians (Center, 2006e), yet media entities often present items that ignore the very existence of APRNs, even in areas where APRNs play a central role, such as primary care for underserved populations. In 2005, the Center and other nurses persuaded the U.S. Department of Health and Human Services to change the name of its annual minority health campaign from "Take a Loved One to the Doctor Day" to "Take a Loved One for a Checkup Day," as noted in the case study (Center, 2005b). The news media may also accept criticism of APRN care by competitors in organized medicine with little or no question, as has often occurred in connection with the growth of APRN-staffed retail-based clinics. Such press pieces often do not even consult APRNs (Center, 2006k).

The prevalence of these stereotypes has a significant negative impact on health care decision-making and nursing. When nurses are seen mainly as low-skilled physician subordinates, their health care expertise has less impact on colleagues, patients, the media, and the public. Nurses also struggle to get the resources they need to provide high-quality direct care, to conduct vital research, and to educate a new generation of nurses.

111

The Challenge of Getting "Real Nursing" into the Media

The question remains: How do we get real nursing into the media, so we can change the population's perception of nursing? This is essential if the voice of nursing in the shaping of health care is to be heard, or at the very least, so the population served values nurses' information and applies it in day-to-day health decision-making. To improve public understanding of nursing and improve health care itself, nurses must become more involved in shaping the media that the public consumes—yet getting nursing into the media is a monumental challenge. Nurses have been reluctant to step forward and reach out to the media. At the same time, the media has failed to seek out nurses for their expert comment, instead consulting physicians on subjects for which nurses are generally more expert. This is presumably a result of the cumulative effect of the stereotypical nursing image just discussed, but it may stem in particular from the belief that nursing is merely a minor subset of medicine, rather than a separate, autonomous profession (Center, 2006f). When nurses have so little independent credibility in the media, it is hard for them to be seen as reliable, knowledgeable health resources by and for their patients.

The Process of Communicating

In mass communication, there is typically a sender, a message, a recipient, and feedback (Reynolds, 1997). The message is crafted to reach certain types of recipients; often, it is aimed at a specific demographic. The message is sent in a specific medium, with the sender making an effort to cut through background noise and clutter. Recipients decode the message in their own way based on the message, the clutter, and the level of credibility of the sender, which affects whether recipients take action on the message in accord with the sender's goals (Freed, 2006).

Under this framework, nurses who wish to communicate must assess their credibility as health educators. Of course, Gallup polls show nurses have a high level of public trust (Saad, 2006)—but trust is not the same as respect. Based on the rampant negative media depictions and relatively low funding for the profession as a whole, it seems that the public trusts nurses to hold their wallets while they are in surgery, but not to play a significant role in keeping patients alive while they are actually in surgery or to educate them about how to recover. True respect for the profession would entail meaningful public inquiry into the nature of nursing work and the people who do it. It would mean serious federal funding to address the global nursing shortage—one of the greatest public health crises in today's world. It would mean incorporation of nurses on every board and committee related to health. It would mean that at least half of every hospital board was composed of nurses. However, because nursing is undervalued, these things are not happening.

The bedrock components of nursing practice are direct patient care, patient education, and patient advocacy. Nursing education, nursing research, and nursing advocacy underpin each of the three components. When nurses advocate for a stronger profession, they are improving their direct care and their ability to educate and advocate for patients. If nurses wish to increase the number of people who take positive action based on their health messages, they must increase their credibility as health educators—and that begins with improving their media image.

If nurses continue to avoid participating in the media, they will miss vital opportunities to reach patients and society with key health information, including information to help the public better understand nursing itself. Patients will lack the information they need to make good health decisions. In recent years, some nurses have worked effectively to communicate about their work, through media such as books, radio shows, op-ed pieces, and public advocacy campaigns (Center, 2006b; 2007a). However, the profession must be far more vocal and assertive if it is to make the sea change in public understanding that the current situation requires.

Nurses Must Improve Nursing's Image in Order to Improve Health Care

Some might ask why nurses have to improve the nursing image in order to get key health messages to patients and the public. The reason is that when nursing is so undervalued in the public consciousness—when people think that only physicians have substantive knowledge about health issues—then nurses' health messages are not heard or acted upon by patients.

Consider the last time you were at a family gathering, neighborhood cookout, or party. It is common for nurses to meet new people or old friends and have the conversation turn to personal health issues. In such situations, nurses have a great opportunity to educate people, one by one, about health issues, and also to establish themselves as health experts. Family, friends, or acquaintances might tell a nurse of their health concerns, and particularly given nursing's strong focus on preventative health and health management, the nurse might be eager to educate as well as possible given the social setting. However, many nurses report that social bias or nursism can work against them in these settings. Nurses often have the sense that their messages are not heard, believed or adopted, even though they were based on evidence and years of advanced training, particularly if the nursing advice appears to be inconsistent with that of a physician.

It would hardly take a logical leap to surmise that the basic reason for this lack of perceived credibility is the huge gulf in the levels of genuine social respect for medicine and nursing. Because nurses are constantly seen as people who do not know anything meaningful or substantive, their expert advice is often ignored or discounted—and needless to say, this problem exists in clinical settings as well; nurses often have the sense that what they tell patients and non-nurse colleagues is discounted in critical decision-making. However, neither patients nor colleagues can afford to undervalue nurses' teaching. It is vital to public health that these recipients hear and heed nurses' messages, many of which the recipients are unlikely to hear anywhere else—and many of which could make the difference between life and death.

If nurses want to reach out to the media and start affecting it, they need to know the nuts and bolts of how the media works. What follows are suggestions to do just this, using the media as a way to educate the populations that nurses serve in their own everyday decision-making.

Every nurse should read and consider the advice in *From Silence to Voice* by Bernice Buresh and Suzanne Gordon, now in its second edition (2006). The authors, experienced journalists who serve on the Center's board of directors, have written a fabulous how-to manual on how the media works and how nurses can better participate in media coverage. This important book shows that nurses have not given the public an adequate account of their work, but it offers strategies to help nurses tell the world what they do, in order to get the resources and respect needed to resolve the nursing crisis and help patients achieve better health.

Interested nurses should also read the excellent fifth edition (2007) of *Policy & Politics in Nursing and Health Care*, edited by Diana Mason, Judith Leavitt, and Mary Chaffee. Especially helpful is Chapter 9: "Harnessing the Power of the Media to Influence Health Policy and Politics" that features information on getting free media coverage, Internet activism, "Talking the Right Talk" by Suzanne Gordon, and a segment on the work of the Center (Mason, Dodd, & Glickstein, 2007).

Nurses who believe they may have the opportunity to speak to the media should consider getting media training. Nurses' employers can encourage such training, and perhaps pay for the costs, in order to help nurses increase understanding of their work and promote the institution by extension. In fact, institutions might consider maintaining a core group of nurses who are skilled at interacting with the media. The Center's media-training resources page, www.nursingadvocacy.org/action/media_training.html, has links to discussions of media myths, media training seminars and workshops, and online resources. Nurses can also get tips on writing powerful letters in the Center's guide at www.nursingadvocacy.org/action/get_help_writing.html.

The following are some specific strategies nurses might use to persuade society that they and their messages are worthy of attention.

Reaching Out to the Media

To get media coverage, nurses must actively seek it. As Buresh and Gordon (2006) show, nurses have traditionally shied away from the media in accord with the prevailing "virtue script," which entails a code of self-effacement. Naturally, physicians and others have been happy to supply the media with input that nurses have declined to provide. This system has not served the profession of nursing well, so nurses must work to make sure they are seen and heard.

Appoint a Public Relations Professional to Promote Nursing

One way to get the word out about the work that nurses do at an institution is to appoint a public relations (PR) person who is dedicated *solely* to that task. Many hospitals have one or more PR professionals who promote physicians and the hospital in general, but there is rarely a focus on nursing. However, Massachusetts General Hospital (MGH) has a PR person dedicated to promoting *only* nursing at the hospital. Other hospitals should be encouraged to follow this example. In October 2005, the *Boston Globe* published an excellent four-part, front-page series on the training of a new ICU nurse. In order to get the story, the *Globe* reporter and photographer spent 9 months following a veteran nurse and her apprentice at MGH. That article was the result of significant effort by MGH's PR director for nursing Georgia Peirce, a member of the Center's board of directors, who spent months convincing the *Globe* to follow nurses and report on their work.

Provide News Resources for the Media

Individual nurses should offer to serve as expert resources for the media. In doing so, nurses should take care to be responsive, reliable, and credible. Specific measures nurses might consider to do this more effectively include:

- Collecting and promoting story ideas to help the media develop stories on nursing, and incorporate a nursing perspective in general health care stories

115

- Building a database of information on local nursing issues to use as a resource for responding to media inquiries
- Creating a roster of nurses who are expert in different fields to have on hand when the media does ask for expert input
- Developing online video news programs or Internet Web sites that depict real images of nursing
- Determining who a media entity's gate keeper or decision-maker is, and arranging to speak to that person
- Issuing press releases that create a framework for a story about nursing and health

One impressive example of this kind of media outreach is the work of the *American Journal of Nursing* (*AJN*) under the leadership of editor-in-chief Diana J. Mason, who sits on the Center's advisory panel. *AJN* has done a fabulous job of communicating with the general media about nursing research and other material appearing in the journal. The *AJN* creates press releases about significant material it runs and regularly contacts the media to pitch stories of interest. A compelling narrative story from *AJN* was republished in the November 2004 *Reader's Digest*, with readership around 80 million (Answers, 2007; Center for Nursing Advocacy, 2004a). The story told how one nurse spurred a declining leukemia patient's recovery after a bone marrow transplant by subtly getting him to engage with her over a cup of tea. The type of media outreach *AJN* does is the method used by physician journals, which is one reason their research receives such widespread press coverage.

Creating Media with Accurate Depictions of Nurses

Nurses must develop media that gives the public an accurate vision of the profession, including both its achievements and its problems. Many types of media can reach out to patients and educate them about health topics or nursing. For example, advertising can be very effective, especially when there is a good match between the medium, the message, and the resources of the advertiser. Television is a powerful way to communicate basic ideas, but it can be expensive unless a broadcaster donates the airtime. It appears to be easier to get donated radio airtime as compared to television. In 2005, the Ad Council reported $1 billion worth of donated radio time, $338 million worth of television and cable airtime, and $30 million worth of space donated by newspapers (Ad Council, 2006). Major newspapers and other publications can reach a significant audience with more complex messages, but they can be expensive. Radio and the Internet may be more affordable ways to reach certain audiences.

Society needs to know that nurses are experts in clinical practice and in health education. Potential ways to advance those goals include health education videos, articles, books (fiction and nonfiction), short stories, guides, television shows, movies (features, shorts, documentaries, animated), novels, plays, poems, Web sites, radio programs, paintings, comics, cartoons, children's interactive CDs (like *Rescue Heroes* for nurses), children's books, children's videos, coloring books, Halloween costumes, dolls, action figures, toys, and board games. Although such media might help to interest career seekers, the profession also needs nurses to create media that presents the challenges and problems that nursing confronts today. See more on creating nursing media at www.nursingadvocacy.org/create/create.html.

An example of a paid advertising campaign with major television and Internet components is Johnson & Johnson's prominent Campaign for Nursing's Future, whose stated goal has been to increase interest in nursing careers. Some elements of this campaign, particularly elements of the campaign's web site (partly created by the Center) and a short video about nurse scientists, contain helpful and persuasive information. As discussed earlier, some believe that the campaign's more influential television advertising spots tend to reinforce angel and handmaiden imagery but J&J has cited research suggesting that its campaign has significantly raised the profile of nursing in certain segments of the community (Center, 2006j).

Of course, shaping the course of existing media activity (paid and unpaid) remains critical because of that media's vast influence, and the fact that it constantly portrays health care, including nurses and nursing. The work of nursing so often is the subject of media attention because it is dramatic and exciting, filled with both intense emotion and cutting-edge technology, life and death, hope and despair. Influencing this media is often the most effective and affordable way to affect the nursing image and to deliver key health messages. Moreover, one of the best ways to advance any cause is earned media; press that those with a given interest generate by doing newsworthy things and encouraging the press to cover them. Of course, media created by those who are not seen to share a specific policy agenda (such as advancing nursing or some health message) can have more credibility with the public. Nurses can make claims about their work, but what the public sees about nursing in major newspapers (or Hollywood dramas) may be taken as a more objective account of the profession.

Though shaping existing media activity does not require direct payments, it can require a tremendous expenditure of time, effort, and skill, as evidenced by the case study presented at the beginning of the chapter. It can take years and more to make a change. The media rarely approaches nurses and asks them how it should portray them or health care generally. Therefore, nurses must work for better treatment of the health issues that matter to them.

Present a Professional Image of Nursing

Before nurses can expect to improve nursing's image, they must examine the image that each of them presents to the world. Some nurses may think professionalism means conforming to a traditional ideal of appearance, such as the white-starched apron and cap. Others may adopt a strict approach toward colleagues, patients, and families, imposing needless restrictions to maintain order, yet many professionals would not define their professions in these terms, but in terms of an unflagging commitment to the best interests of those they serve.

Part of any profession's image relates to the appearance of its members, and this may be particularly true for groups that do not enjoy automatic respect. If nurses want respect, they should strive to look like college-educated science professionals, as physicians and others in the clinical setting do. Some nurses wear patterned scrubs, and of course, the media often portrays nurses as doing so. One late 2006 episode of ER presented a resident physician who was mortified that, because her usual clothes had become messy at the hospital, she had to wear patterned scrubs that made her look like a nurse. Unsurprisingly, she was mocked by another physician. Many feel that patterned scrubs say "disrespect me!" to the public, just as the similar-looking 1960s housedresses said about homemakers.

Another important element of nurses' professional appearance is recognition in clinical settings that a nurse actually is a nurse. This is especially important because of the recent proliferation of other hospital workers, particularly unlicensed assistive personnel who may do tasks formerly done by nurses. Nurses need to take ownership of their own image, and it is not in the profession's interest for nurses to be confused with others in the clinical setting. Nurses should consider wearing the "RN" patch created in 2003 by Mark Dion and J. Morgan Puett, in collaboration with the Fabric Workshop and Museum in Philadelphia. The Center has crafted various versions of the RN patch for nurses with different educational credentials to help teach patients (and remind fellow health professionals) that it takes rigorous education to become a nurse. See more on uniforms and the RN patches at www.nursingadvocacy.org/action/RN_patch.html.

Nurses and others should also consider what messages their choice of language may send. When we suggest "nurse-friendly" language, we of course do not mean language that is nice to nurses, but language that reflects recognition that nurses are highly skilled health professionals who save lives and improve outcomes. (Similarly, "user-friendly" does not mean language that is nice to users, but language that helps them work effectively.) The nurse-friendly language section on frequently asked questions on the Center's Web site encourages the use of language that sends an accurate message about nurses and their role in health care. Some questions tackled are: "Are nurses who don't work at the bedside 'real nurses'?" "Should we refer to physician or nurse practitioner care plans as 'orders' (or prescriptions)?" See more on nurse-friendly language at www.nursingadvocacy.org/faq/nf/nf.html.

Nursing's Influence on the Health Care Decisions of Others

If nurses succeed in reducing the impact of the current stereotypes of their profession, nurses' voices will increasingly be recognized for what they are, and not seen as the natterings of some degraded fictional vision of nursing. Nurses then will be seen as valuable and reliable sources of information who can guide others in making important health decisions.

However, nurses must keep in mind that engaging with health-related media entails both opportunities and responsibilities. If the lay media is currently covering a health story or piece of research, people are very likely to start asking health professionals about it. At least 80 percent of adults who use the Internet have done so to research health issues, and health care information is the third most common reason for these adults' Internet usage (Pew Internet & American Life Project, 2003). Few nurses have been spared probing questions from Internet-educated patients about diseases or other health topics. Nurses must make efforts to stay connected to the information that the individuals they serve are accessing, so that nurses are conversant with new developments and able to respond to questions and concerns. Of course, it can be dangerous to rely on a lay media reporter's interpretation of a health care study, so nurses should go straight to the research when getting health information to make sure they understand and can explain it to patients better. Lay media articles almost always include the name of the underlying resource—usually a published article in a health care journal. Most hospitals and schools have subscriptions to major databases so nurses can access articles at no cost. Connecting patients to evidence-based information is critical to nurses' role in helping them make health care decisions.

Not all health-related media on the Internet is as accurate as it should be. When people come to nurses with health information from the Internet, nurses might advise them to look for the logo of the Health on the Net Foundation, an international nonprofit organization that works to verify the reliability of Internet health information. Information on the organization can be found at www.hon.ch. Readers can look for the Health on the Net logo, and click on it at a given web site to verify that the site is registered with the organization. If so, readers can have some confidence that the web site at least strives to deliver accurate and evidence-based health care information.

Nurses also must take active steps to shape the health information individuals see on the Internet and in other media. If the information is not accurate or complete, nurses should try to provide better information by working with the media using the suggestions given previously.

Send Feedback to the Media

It is important that nurses let the media know that they are watching, and that they expect the media to present a fair and accurate account of the profession, especially at a time when nursing is under great stress. Nurses should monitor the media and send feedback. Some examples include sending thanks to the media for accurate or three-dimensional coverage of nursing issues; providing feedback to journalists, individuals, or groups who are responsible for inaccurate or damaging depictions of nurses, as the case study presented earlier illustrates; and mobilize colleagues to protest poor portrayals of nursing.

Remember that even the entertainment and advertising media have powerful effects on public views of nursing and health, and many people are more likely to engage with health issues that are set in the context of popular entertainment. Many of us are more focused on what's happening on *Grey's Anatomy* than we are on the nightly news, and calling attention to how such entertainment products treat nursing can generate vital public discussion of nursing and its situation.

Conclusion

The media influences health care decisions, so nurses have an important responsibility to advocate for more accurate media depictions of nurses and nursing, as well as more accurate and complete messages that will support better decision-making in health care generally. As the "Take a Loved One for a Checkup Day" campaign shows, changing social perceptions through the media takes time, commitment, and a sustained, cohesive strategy. However, nurses *can* do it.

References

Ad Council. (2006). *PSA bulletin: 2005 record-breaking year in donated media*. Retrieved February 14, 2007, from www.adcouncil.org/psab/2006_July_August

Answers. (2007.) *Reader's Digest*. Retrieved February 15, 2007, from www.answers.com/topic/reader-s-digest

Brodie, M., Foehr, U., Rideout, V., Baer, N., Miller, C., Flournoy, R., & Altman, D. (2001). Communicating health information through the entertainment media. *Health Affairs*, 20(1), 192–199. Retrieved February 19, 2007, from http://content.healthaffairs.org/cgi/reprint/20/1/192

Buresh, B., & Gordon, S. (2006). *From silence to voice: What nurses know and must communicate to the public*, 2nd ed. Ithaca, NY: ILR Press.

Center for Nursing Advocacy. (2003a). *One flew over the cuckoo's nest review*. Retrieved February 19, 2007, from www.nursingadvocacy.org/media/films/cuckoos_nest.html

Center for Nursing Advocacy. (2003b). *Washington Post highlights center's "ER" campaign*. Retrieved February 25, 2007, from www.nursingadvocacy.org/news/2003nov18_washpost.html

Center for Nursing Advocacy. (2004a). *Killers, tea and sympathy*. Retrieved February 15, 2007, from www.nursingadvocacy.org/news/2004nov/rd.html

Center for Nursing Advocacy. (2004b). *Kicking Dr. Phil's ass to the curb*. Retrieved February 19, 2007, from www.nursingadvocacy.org/news/2004nov/18_dr_phil.html

Center for Nursing Advocacy. (2005a). *Take a loved one for a checkup day*. Retrieved February 11, 2007, from www.nursingadvocacy.org/news/2005jul/loved_one.html

Center for Nursing Advocacy. (2005b). *Babynewspaper*. Retrieved February 19, 2007, from www.nursingadvocacy.org/news/2005dec/04_balt_sun.html

Center for Nursing Advocacy. (2006a). *Why aren't you more excited that public opinion polls often put nurses at the top of the list of "most trusted" and "most ethical" professions?* Retrieved February 14, 2007, from www.nursingadvocacy.org/faq/most_trusted.html

Center for Nursing Advocacy. (2006b). *Golden lamp awards: Best media depictions of nursing 2006."* Retrieved February 14, 2007, from www.nursingadvocacy.org/press/releases/golden/2006/awd.html#best

Center for Nursing Advocacy. (2006c). *ER television review*. Retrieved February 19, 2007, from www.nursingadvocacy.org/media/tv/er.html

Center for Nursing Advocacy. (2006d). *What's the big deal about 'naughty nurse' images in the media? I mean, no one believes nurses really dress like that!* Retrieved February 19, 2007, from www.nursingadvocacy.org/faq/naughty_nurse.html

Center for Nursing Advocacy. (2006e). *Do physicians deliver better care than advanced practice nurses?* Retrieved February 19, 2007, from www.nursingadvocacy.org/faq/apn_md_relative_merits.html

Center for Nursing Advocacy. (2006f). *Are you sure nurses are autonomous? Based on what I've seen, it sure looks like physicians are calling the shots*. Retrieved February 25, 2007, from www.nursingadvocacy.org/faq/autonomy.html

Center for Nursing Advocacy. (2006g). *Family presence and the physician in charge*. Retrieved on February 26, 2007, from www.nursingadvocacy.org/news/2006/apr/03_new_yorker.html

Center for Nursing Advocacy. (2006h). *CVS pharmacist returns from Matrix; can now download entire nursing curriculum into your brain in four hours!* Retrieved February 19, 2007, from www.nursingadvocacy.org/news/2006/jan/24_cvs.html

Center for Nursing Advocacy. (2006i). *Touching the world*. Retrieved February 19, 2007, from www.nursingadvocacy.org/media/commercials/jnj_2005.html

Center for Nursing Advocacy. (2006j). *Response from Johnson & Johnson*. Retrieved February 14, 2007, from www.nursingadvocacy.org/media/commercials/jnj_2005_response.html

Center for Nursing Advocacy. (2006k). *But when I became a physician, I put away nursing things*. Retrieved February 19, 2007, from www.nursingadvocacy.org/news/2006/jul/08_houston_chron.html

Center for Nursing Advocacy. (2006l). *Debugging the "electronic nurse."* Retrieved February 19, 2007, from www.nursingadvocacy.org/news/2006/sep/20_electronic_nurse.html

Center for Nursing Advocacy. (2007a). *Annual Golden Lamp Awards—Best media depictions of nursing*. Retrieved February 14, 2007, from www.nursingadvocacy.org/press/releases/golden/lamp_awards.html

Center for Nursing Advocacy. (2007b). *News on nursing in the media*. Retrieved on February 26, 2007, from www.nursingadvocacy.org/news/news.html

Center for Nursing Advocacy. (2007c). The work of Beatrice Kalisch and Philip Kalisch on nursing's public image and the nursing shortage. Retrieved May 8, 2007, from www.nursingadvocacy.org/research/lit/kalisch_kalisch.html

Darbyshire, P., & Gordon, S. (2005). Exploring popular images and reputations of nurses and nursing. In J. Daly, et al. (Eds.). *Professional nursing: Concepts, issues, and challenges*. (pp. 69–92). New York: Springer Publishing Company.

Freed, J. (2006). *Model of the communication cycle: Communication creates reality*. Retrieved February 11, 2007 from www.media-visions.com/communication.html

Glik, D. C. (2003). *Health communication in popular media formats*. American Public Health Association Annual Meeting presentation. Retrieved February 11, 2007, from www.medscape.com/viewarticle/466709

Henry J. Kaiser Family Foundation (2004). *Entertainment education and health in the United States*. Retrieved February 19, 2007, from www.kff.org/entmedia/7047.cfm

Henry J. Kaiser Family Foundation. (2003). *Survey of ER viewers: Summary of results*. Retrieved February 19, 2007, from www.kff.org/womenshealth/1358-ers.cfm

Henry J. Kaiser Family Foundation. (2002). *The impact of TV's health content: A case study of ER viewers*. Retrieved February 19, 2007, from www.kff.org/entmedia/3230-index.cfm

HHS Press Office. (2004). HHS Secretary Tommy G. Thompson launches third annual "take a loved one to the doctor day." Retrieved February 15, 2007, from www.blackamericaweb.com/site.aspx/health/drday/drdayrel

JWT Communications. (2000). *Memo to nurses for a healthier tomorrow coalition members on a focus group study of 1800 school children in 10 U.S. cities*. Retrieved February 19, 2007, from www.nursingadvocacy.org/research/lit/jwt_memo1.html

Kalisch, P. A., & Kalisch, B. J. (1986). A comparative analysis of nurse and physician characters in the entertainment media. *Journal of Advanced Nursing, 11*(2), 179–195.

Lewenson, S. B. (1993). *Taking charge: Nursing, suffrage, and feminism in America, 1873–1920.* New York: Garland Press.

Mason, D. J., Dodd, C. J., & Glickstein, B. (2007). Harnessing the power of the media to influence health policy and politics. In D. J. Mason, J. K. Leavitt, & M. W. Chafee (Eds.), *Policy and politics in nursing and health care* (5th ed.). (pp. 149–168). St. Louis, MO: Saunders Elsevier.

Mason, D. J., Leavitt, J. K., & Chafee, M. W. (Eds.). (2007). *Policy and politics in nursing and health care,* 5th ed. St. Louis, MO: Saunders Elsevier.

Nelson, S., & Gordon, S. (2006). *The complexities of care: Nursing reconsidered.* Ithaca, NY: Cornell University Press.

Newspaper Association of America Foundation. (2005). *Speaking of a free press: 200 years of notable quotations about press freedoms,* p. 3. Retrieved February 23, 2007, from www.naafoundation.org/pdf/Speaking_of_a_Free_Press.pdf

Pew Internet & American Life Project. (2003). *Internet health resources.* Retrieved February 23, 2007, from www.pewinternet.org/PPF/r/95/report_display.asp

Reynolds, K. (1997). *What is the transmission model of interpersonal communication and what is wrong with it?* Student paper from the University of Wales, Aberystwyth. Retrieved February 11, 2007, from www.aber.ac.uk/media/Students/kjr9601.html

Saad, L. (2006). *Gallup Poll news service: Nurses top list of most honest and ethical professions: Integrity of most medical professionals also highly rated.* Retrieved February 25, 2007, from www.galluppoll.com/content/default.aspx?ci=25888&VERSION=p

Turow, J., & Gans, R. (2002). *As seen on TV: Health policy issues in TV's medical dramas.* Report to the Henry J. Kaiser Family Foundation, p. 1. Retrieved February 11, 2007, from www.kff.org/entmedia/3231-index.cfm

U.S. Census Bureau. (2007). *Statistical abstract of the United States.* Section 24. "Media Usage and Consumer Spending: 2000 to 2009," Table 1110. Retrieved February 1, 2007, from www.census.gov/prod/2006pubs/07statab/infocomm.pdf

U.S. Department of Health and Human Services, Health Resources and Service Administration, Bureau of Health Professions, Division of Nursing. (2000). *The registered nurse population: Findings from the national sample survey of registered nurses.* Retrieved July 20, 2007, from http://bhpr.hrsa.gov/healthworkforce/reports/rnsurvey/rnss1.htm

Young, R. (2006). "Google . . . the OS for advertising." Retrieved February 11, 2007, from http://gigaom.com/2006/11/09/google-the-os-for-advertising

Index